HELP.

HER.

HEAL

AN EMPATHY WORKBOOK FOR SEX ADDICTS

TO HELP THEIR PARTNERS HEAL.

BY: CAROL JUERGENSEN SHEETS LCSW, CSAT, CCPS, PCC

WITH ALLAN J. KATZ LPC, CSAT

SANO PRESS, LLC
LONG BEACH, CA

SANO PRESS, LLC
LONG BEACH, CA

1st Edition

Cover spread, book design, & layout by Chris Bordey.
All images from Pixabay.com, Unsplash.com, and Flaticon.com in accordance with Creative Commons CC0 except where noted. "Primary Feelings" graphics (p. 35, 36, 38, 40, 42, 44) by Chris Bordey. Sano feather trademark Sano Family and Therapy P.C.

ISBN-13: 978-1-7339222-0-3
ISBN-10: 1-7339222-0-2

"TO ME, THE THING THAT IS WORSE THAN DEATH IS BETRAYAL...
I CAN CONCEIVE DEATH, BUT I COULD NOT CONCEIVE BETRAYAL."

—MALCOLM X

TABLE OF CONTENTS

7. CONFLICT

8. TECHNIQUES THAT KEEP YOU STRONG WHILE YOU HELP HER HEAL

9. WAYS TO DEVELOP INTIMACY

10. PROCESSES THAT MUST OCCUR BEFORE EARLY RECOVERY COUPLE'S WORK.......................... 153

11. RITUALS THAT PROMOTE CONNECTION, TRUST, AND RESTORATION OF THE RELATIONSHIP

A NOTE FROM CAROL:

I am excited to help you through the arduous process of learning empathy. I wrote this workbook to help male addicts reduce their shame by helping their partners work through the pain.
These are the tools to make that happen.

IT IS THE
ADDICT
THAT
CARRIES
THE SHAME

BUT IT IS
THE
PARTNER
THAT
CARRIES
THE PAIN.

-CAROL JUERGENSEN SHEETS LCSW, CSAT, CCPS, PCC

WELCOME TO THIS WORKBOOK

First of all, congratulations on owning this book. This may be the first real step you have taken to invest in your coupleship, and you now understand that you need a guide to teach you. If you are like most sex addicts who walk into my office, you have come here with or without your spouse to learn how to manage your addiction. Most addicts don't seek counseling until their addiction is discovered. Most times, this involves the spouse. Perhaps she saw a text from an affair partner, or receipt from a massage parlor, or a notification from a website. Equal to the desire to change is the desire to keep your marriage together. Although you haven't asked about it directly, you want to know how you can make amends or ease the devastating pain that she is experiencing. Your self-esteem is in the gutter because of the addiction and because you have caused what appears to be irreparable damage. Your wife is unable to sleep, and she has not been able to stop asking questions that are painful to both her and to you. Her emotions vacillate, and she seems to go from acting indifferent to name calling within nanoseconds. She is crying, yelling, or shutting down, and you don't know what to do to slow this emotional roller coaster.

Whether you are here as a result of the discovery or because she has told you to seek help, you realize that you have caused great pain and you want guidance to reassure her that you will not hurt her again.

The truth of the matter is that you will hurt her again. You will do something today that will trigger the emotional cycle again. It may not make sense to you because you don't understand what may have set her off, but something will trigger her, and she will revisit the wound, re-rupturing an already ruptured relationship.

Please note that you can use this book by yourself to work on developing empathy. However, it is important to get counseling from a therapist who has been trained in a partner-sensitive approach. You can scroll to the end of the book to find two organizations that have expertise in providing early couples recovery work. If at all possible, work with a trained professional in partner-sensitive therapy.

UNDERSTANDING EACH OTHER'S PAIN IS THE FASTEST WAY TO RECOVERY.

—REBECCA ROSENBLAT

EMPATHY TO THE RESCUE!

THE ANECDOTE FOR ADDICTION IS CONNECTION

You and your partner cannot experience connection until she knows that she is safe. It is an arduous task to rebuild trust. Empathy is the key to re-establishing that trust so that you will be able to handle the storm of betrayal trauma and help when she is totally "in the weeds" with pain.

WHAT IS EMPATHY?

Basically, gaining empathy means that you must make a specialized effort to see the world through the eyes of your partner. This requires asking yourself, "How does my partner feel at all times?" It is imperative to see it from her perspective. You want to put yourself in her shoes to the best of your ability and describe how you have made her feel.

In a normal empathetic exchange, a person would describe what he or she believes the other person is feeling. However, your situation is different, because in many cases your actions have caused betrayal injury and you can only *imagine* how that could feel.

The exercises in this book will teach you to meet her where she is. If she is unbelievably angry, you will need to let her know that you see her anger AND you know you caused her that pain. Sex addicts in recovery can be containers for the pain and avoid immersing themselves in the shame. This lets the spouse know that their choice to share feelings is welcomed in the relationship.

You see, in healthy relationships, "conflict breeds intimacy," so the hope is that you can restore your relationship and bring it into a state of health and well-being. Then, when conflict occurs, you will have the strength to know that even though it feels scary, once it is externalized and you work on your empathy, your spouse will feel safe and your relationship will move towards more closeness.

> THE GOAL OF EMPATHY AND INTIMACY: TO RESTORE THE RELATIONSHIP AND BRING IT BACK INTO A STATE OF HEALTH AND WELL-BEING. WHEN CONFLICT OCCURS FROM BETRAYAL TRAUMA, YOU WILL HAVE THE STRENGTH TO CONNECT THROUGH EMPATHY, LEAVING YOUR WIFE FEELING A RENEWED SENSE OF SAFETY AND YOUR RELATIONSHIP FEELING MORE INTIMATE.

This is a huge undertaking and typically requires the assistance of a good therapist to navigate through your partner's feelings. You have traumatized her and now you must prove that you can meet her emotional needs for perhaps the first time.

So many women confide in me that they despise the "acting out," but what they can't live with is the manipulation and gaslighting that occurs while their husbands act out. They report that their husbands made them feel crazy when they asked too many questions or shared their fears that something was not right. Now that you are in recovery, you will need to learn to be direct and ask questions to clarify how she feels, and send her the message that her needs really matter.

CHAPTER 1
YOUR ADDICTION

HOW DID THIS BEHAVIOR BECOME SO OUT OF CONTROL?

Sex addiction has always existed, but it did not become widespread until the late 1990's because of the INTERNET. You may have heard that sexual addiction is so much more prevalent today because of the 3 A's: It is Affordable, it can be Anonymous, and it is forever Accessible. Experiencing the pitfalls of sexual addiction can help you create boundaries around your behavior that will increase success in your recovery.

Now imagine how your partner feels because she too knows how easy it is for you to slip. She is on edge most of her waking hours because she realizes that these temptations are available to you at a moments notice. It can feel overwhelming to her and keep her in a state of terror that she will "discover" your slip or relapse and won't be able to bear it. That is why your mission is to maintain good recovery. You have the power to decrease your temptations and to reduce her fears by practicing techniques that ensure your success. If she is going to stay in this relationship, her well-being depends on your recovery!

ACCESSIBILITY

You can limit the damage by doing whatever it takes to cut off accessibility. Volunteering to put a GPS on your phone or in your car will allow her to "track" you and reassure herself that you are exactly where you need to be. Taking pictures of yourself at a moment's notice will help her to increase her confidence in the relationship. By making yourself accessible to her, you will be limiting the accessibility to act out.

AFFORDABILITY

We all know that sexual addiction does not have to cost a dime, yet as the disorder progressed, it has likely cost you money that you never thought you would spend. Addiction is progressive; it always gets worse. "Free pornography" can become paid subscriptions or downloads that cost money. Experimenting by checking out strip clubs may have turned into visits to massage parlors with "happy endings." You may have visited and explored chat rooms which resulted in paid escorts or prostitution. Again, as the addiction progressed, so have the emotional and financial costs and the betrayal factor. Now that you have come clean, it is important to give your partner direct access to your financial status. She may need to take over the bills. She should be able to monitor accounts day or night, go run credit checks whenever she needs to reassure herself that you can be trusted.

Giving her this freedom shows that you are sensitive to her needs for safety and security, and that you are empathizing with her need to minimize her fears.

ANONYMITY

One of the hardest things for her to reconcile is the illusion she had of the man she thought you were versus the real man you really are—the man suffering from sexual addiction. You thought you could keep your secret forever. You lived in a world of denial. You assumed that you could have two lives. The addiction caused you to have "stinking thinking" which denied the reality that someday you would be discovered, and destroy her life and your relationship. You have lived a dual life, and this duality frightened her and made her question herself and her sense of reality. She wonders who you are and how could she have entrusted herself, her children, and her life to a man she didn't know.

ARE YOU WILLING TO DO WHAT IT WILL TAKE?

Now that she has discovered what you have really been doing, you will need to do whatever it takes to redefine yourself in recovery.

There are three phases to restoring the relationship after discovery: A period of time where you have sustained good recovery so that she has more assurance that you want to get healthy and are willing to do what it takes to provide her a sense of safety and stabilization. She needs to know that you have proper supports in place to be healthy. Patrick Carnes says that your recovery is dependent on a strong support system, which he calls "the committee." You will need to build a strong "committee" to assist you through the transformation that it takes to maintain good sobriety. He says that no one is strong enough to do it alone and that although there are lots of ways to build support, the 12-Step process has proven itself over many decades. Support groups like Sex Addicts Anonymous, Sexaholic's Anonymous, Every Man's Battle, Recovery Nation, and L.I.F.E. Recovery International are also available to help you with this process.

YOU NEED TO PROVIDE TRUTH WHICH BUILDS IN SAFETY

Once you have established some solid recovery, you will need to participate in a formal disclosure with a partner sensitive trained therapist who will provide your partner appropriate safety and stabilization while she hears the entire truth for the first time. The process of a formal disclosure requires that you have a therapist who has been trained in a partner sensitive approach.

> A FORMAL DISCLOSURE ALLOWS THE PARTNER TO HEAR THE TRUTH SO THAT SHE CAN DECIDE HOW SHE IS GOING TO PROCEED IN HER LIFE AND IN HER RELATIONSHIP.

Many times, the disclosure is followed by an emotional impact letter that is written by your partner after the disclosure. This is a tool that the addict can use to address the pain that the partner deals with on a daily basis. It is a great way to begin the process of empathy, as it gives her a chance to formally address her devastation, trauma and pain.

Next in response, you will write a restitution letter. This exercise will show your wife that you recognize her pain and that you are willing to make amends. We will explore the intricacies of this process later.

If you want to work on the relationship and make the genuine commitment to the skills of good communication, empathy, and honesty, you will need to practice the life skills in this book. This requires a structured plan to change your life.

IF YOU PRACTICE THESE STRATEGIES, IT WILL ALLOW YOU TO CONTRIBUTE TO YOUR RELATIONSHIP IN A WAY THAT YOU NEVER THOUGHT WAS POSSIBLE!

True empathy means being transparent and honest with her. Let her know that you recognize her fears and doubts. Reassure her that you will do everything possible to rebuild your fractured relationship. You will never again lie to her or mislead her, and you realize that this may take years to rebuild.

 YOUR WILLINGNESS EXERCISE

You have probably heard in your support groups about the many ways an addict can assist his wife in feeling safe. Take a few minutes to list the things that you can do to increase her sense of safety and security. If you are having trouble coming up with a good list, ask your fellowship what they have done. And of course, after exhausting all the possibilities yourself, you can always ask your wife for additional suggestions.

I AM WILLING...

Ex. I am willing to give her all my pass codes to my accounts.

I am willing to take regular polygraph tests.

I am willing to go back to using a flip-phone.

1.

2.

3.

4.

5.

6.

7.

8.

9.

10.

I AM WILLING...

12.

13.

14.

15.

16.

17.

18.

19.

20.

21.

22.

23.

24.

25.

CHECK YOUR MOTIVATION AT THE DOOR

It is important for you to stay the course and practice motivation every time you have the opportunity to use empathy. Once you have established good recovery, you must use empathy every chance that you get.

USING THE FIVE A'S TO ENSURE THAT YOU ARE USING EMPATHY WITH YOUR PARTNER

When you are conversing with your spouse, you might ask yourself:

AWARENESS	Am I aware that I might be able to use empathy here?
ACCEPTANCE	Am I willing to risk the vulnerability to practice empathy for my partner?
ACCOUNTABILITY	How can I take full responsibility and find a way to convey that I empathize with her?
ACKNOWLEDGEMENT	What can I say that lets her know that I am fully aware of the damage that I have caused?
ACTION PLAN	What can I do to assure her that I have changed and that she can trust me?

Now that you and your partner are working through the pain of sexual betrayal, it will be necessary to check your own ability to be the new and improved partner. As a clinician working in this field for over a decade, I know that recovery is tough, but relationship building is tougher because it entails either building on skills you once had or learning skills that you never attained.

The good news is that you are reading this book, practicing the skills and dealing with the mistrust, fear, and sadness that occurs when you are rebuilding a relationship after betrayal. True empathy not only requires that you show your spouse that you put her needs first, but that you show you are confident and remorseful, even when she attacks you out of fear and vulnerability.

UNDERSTANDING THAT POSITIVE CHANGE CAN EVOKE FEAR, FOREBODING JOY

Brené Brown, a social researcher on shame and vulnerability, reports that there is a concept of "foreboding joy" that is frightening and difficult to manage. As you improve at rebuilding the relationship, your partnership will also improve. However this can be accompanied by an intense fear that this joy will not last. Your vulnerable partner may reject it because she is not willing to be duped again. Using empathy statements such as, "I know it may be hard to believe that I am being honest here because I have lied to you so much in the past, but I want you to know that I really do want to prove that I am willing to do whatever it takes to rebuild the trust that I once had" can be a source of reassurance that you understand why she would have trouble trusting you.

Sometimes the partner will respond with "I will never trust you!" When this occurs, you may think that you have shattered any chance of reconciliation. The truth of the matter is that she is protecting herself and letting you know that she fears that the worst is inevitable. She may say "I am only staying with you because of the kids," so that you won't have "one up" on her. This is an opportunity for you to wear your Teflon and to say, "I can't blame you for feeling that way, and I want you to know that I realize that you deserve honesty and authenticity from me no matter what. I am going to work hard on my recovery even if you are only staying with me 'for the kids'."

BASIC TECHNIQUES FOR BUILDING EMPATHY

Sex addicts need to assist in the co-regulation of their partner by using some basic techniques:

- Eye contact

- Warm facial expression

- Caring body language

- Soothing or soft volume

- Touch with permission

When your wife is dis-regulated it can be difficult to practice using these basic techniques. If she is criticizing you, you may have a tendency to look down as opposed to using direct eye contact. She may accuse you of things and your normal reaction might be to raise your voice so that she will hear you. It is so important for you to respond with softness and compassion using with these basic skills. Work diligently to stay non-defensive. Keep your volume soft and caring, give her plenty of space to vent and show her through your eyes and caring body language that you see her pain.

HOW CAN IT RESTORE TRUST?

When you relate with full accountability for your actions in a non-defensive way—with good eye contact and caring body language—you are showing her that you are aware of her pain. When seeing the world from her perspective, she will eventually begin to trust that you are the new and improved version of yourself. While you wounded her on so many levels, the intent here is not to make you feel shamed or blamed. The intent is to help you to recognize the wounding so that you can tell her when you see it.

HOW HAVE I WOUNDED MY SPOUSE?

An instrumental question that you must ask yourself and be able to fully comprehend is, *how have I wounded my spouse?* This exercise is painful because it can take you directly to your guilt and shame, but it is important because it keeps you inherently connected to her pain and her wounding.

Before you can "automatically" default to the empathy formula that we will talk about in this book, you will need to complete this exercise. It will be painful for you, but I ask you to put yourself in her shoes and go back in time to the dreaded day that she learned about your sexual addiction. Perhaps she discovered it or perhaps you shared it with her because you could no longer stand the dark side of yourself.

But go back, remember that time, and write out at least 25 ways that your betrayal and addiction wounded her.

WHEN MY WIFE DISCOVERED MY SEXUAL ADDICTION, SHE FELT WOUNDED BECAUSE....
1.
2.
3.
4.
5.
6.

7.

8.

9.

10.

11.

12.

13.

14.

15.

16.

17.

18.

19.

20.

21.

22.

23.

24.

25.

When you wounded your wife, it automatically left her feeling as if there must have been something wrong with her. She likely thought that she was not enough—sexual enough, young enough, or smart enough. She probably questioned her looks, her intelligence, her worthiness, and her relationship with you. Perhaps the greatest injustice is that she doubted herself and her ability to perceive her life, her relationship, and the world. She no longer knows what is real. She no longer can trust herself or her intuition. I hope that you have added this to your list of wounding.

TAKING A LOOK AT YOUR TIMELINE FROM YOUR PERSPECTIVE (& USING THE EYES OF YOUR PARTNER TO HIGHLIGHT THE SPECIAL/DIFFICULT MOMENTS)

Now I would like you to think back to the beginning of the relationship and create two timelines that parallel each other.

THE FIRST TIMELINE: OUR HISTORY

In the first timeline you will identify pivotal moments that made your marriage unique. Think back through your relationship and think of events that were critical to your coupleship, both good and bad, joyous and difficult.

In the first timeline, notate the first time you:

- Saw your spouse
- Asked her out on a date
- Had your first kiss
- Had your first sexual encounter
- Became exclusive

- Met the parents or family
- Committed to her
- Proposed to your spouse
- Shared your first home together

THE SECOND TIMELINE: MY SEXUAL ADDICTION

For the second timeline, I would like for you to create a continuum that describes your addiction. What lies did you tell her to deceive her? How did you sustain your addiction and yet carry on the façade of being a good husband, provider, family man, business leader, church leader, etc.?

- When did you first act out?
- How might you have lied to her to keep her from knowing your secrets?
- Record times you stayed home from family events, lied about business trips, and times that you almost got caught.

Name the different acting out occurrences and plot them according to the events that you just described in your first timeline. Women often describe the betrayal they felt when you acted out at the bachelor party or while she was in the hospital giving birth to your child or after the promotion that involved business trips.

TIMELINE 1: **OUR HISTORY**	📅 YEAR	TIMELINE 2: **MY SEXUAL ADDICTION**

YOUR PARTNER BELIEVES THAT YOUR ENTIRE RELATIONSHIP WAS AN ILLUSION

This exercise is to help you understand that your partners greatest wounding is believing that nothing that she experienced with you was real. It is to remind you to have empathy for her pain. It is to give you a picture of the betrayal that she has felt because of your acting out and to illustrate to you that her entire perception of the marriage now feels like an illusion. She is mourning the marriage that she thought that she had. This process is here to help you relate to the anger and sadness that she feels about your addiction. It illustrates why she feels so wounded and cannot trust you. And now she can no longer trust herself!

When you develop the muscle of empathy you will be able to easily understand why she fears trusting you. In conjunction with empathy, you will need to allow her the anger, grief, sadness, and despair that she feels. It will likely take lots of time to renegotiate her trust and safety.

The key is for you to empathize and understand without going into self-loathing. Sexual addiction is a relational betrayal and it has caused a huge cavern of doubt for her. Should she stay? Should she leave? What if the kids find out? What kind of example is she setting for her daughters? Is she settling, and why would she do that? Your spouse is questioning everything about herself, you, and your relationship. She is not even able to trust her own reality. Her world feels extremely frightening. The trauma is overwhelming and exhaustive.

You will learn skills in this book that will teach you how to sit with her and her agony. You will have to remain present and know that your current recovery will provide you the backbone to experience her pain. Remember that when she gets activated and goes into a tirade, you must let her know how sorry you feel for having caused such great pain. You will need to do this over and over again.

When she is having a flashback, this timeline will help you remember the many ways that you deceived her. You will then be able to make statements that convey your empathy for her feelings.

For example, if you come home late and she starts to scream and call you a liar, or perhaps tell you that she suspects that you were acting out, you will be able to go back and let her know that of course it would be tough to trust you because you lied so many times about staying late at work. Your timeline will be a reminder of the hundreds of lies you told to sustain your acting out.

Couples make mistakes and hurt each other even in normal relationships. When this occurs, it is your responsibility to figure out how you can "right the wrong," or in other words make it right. Maybe that means a do-over where you get to restate your feelings or a request. Maybe that means that you clarify your issues and feelings so your partner realizes that it hurt your feelings and that is why you were short, insensitive, or angry. Perhaps you just agree to disagree!

John Gottman talks about behavioral repair attempts. When you hurt your partner, you figure out what it would take to clear up the situation and start over. He says that in 85% of all marital arguments, you don't resolve the issue, but you do express your grievances and agree to move forward. The marital homeostasis is very strong and resilient and can weather a lot of conflict. However, in sexual addiction, there is so much wounding that the homeostasis is skewed, and the addict must weather the consequences of his acting out and "do what it takes" initially to show the spouse that he is sensitive to the partner's needs.

THE MOST IMPORTANT THING TO KNOW

Partners consistently report that the #1 thing that they need from their spouse is the acknowledgment that the addict "knows" that the current pain that she is experiencing was a result of his poor choices.

The partner shares how tough it is to go through this agony on a daily basis and not have the addict comment about it. The addict says "I am afraid to comment on it because I don't want to bring it up and activate her," but in reality, it soothes her and gives her strength when he himself is able to recognize and acknowledge!

AN ADDICT WHO CAN SAY "MY WIFE NEEDS TO KNOW THAT I REALIZE THAT I CAUSED HER THIS PAIN" WILL BE IN A BETTER POSITION TO HELP HER WITH HER PAIN.

In this workbook you will learn two important skills—AVR and Trigger Busters—that will help you to work through this heartbreak. They will teach you to respond appropriately to her pain and take full responsibility for it. But first, we need to help you learn more about empathy, so you will be prepared to use these techniques.

 # EMPATHY STATEMENTS EXERCISE

It can be difficult to know what to say when your wife is in so much pain. It takes practice to know what to say and to use empathy when she is hurting. This exercise is to help you create statements that will fit her level of wounding and reassure her that you know that you are the source of her pain. Here are some examples of empathy statements that my clients have used to acknowledge her pain.

- I can see that you are triggered, and I am so sorry that I have caused you this pain.

- I realize that your anger has been caused by my actions in the past.

- I hate that I have done this to you and created all this insecurity.

- I am so sorry that you have to go through this because of me.

- I want you to realize that I hate that I did this to you.

WHAT ARE SOME EMPATHY STATEMENTS THAT YOU CAN USE TO ACKNOWLEDGE YOUR PARTNER'S PAIN?
1.
2.
3.
4.
5.
6.
7.
8.
9.
10.

Don't shortchange yourself here. Really spend some time thinking over her wounding in the previous section so that you can practice knowing what to say.

CHAPTER 2
YOUR FEELINGS

GUILT, SHAME AND SELF-LOATHING

Addicts typically talk about feeling ineffective in making their wife feel safe. They report that she cannot seem to get past her anger and anxiousness. They fear that they have done too much damage, and wonder if they are creating further harm by staying in the relationship. Although these thoughts can be normal, my experience is that these kinds of relationships can be restored—if the partner can be made to feel safe. She needs to see you work on being open, vulnerable, authentic. She needs to see that you are putting her needs first while working on creating a strong recovery program. She will require that you check in with her regularly, be able to express your feelings and honor her feelings. This means that you must know your feelings and not let the shame block your ability to identify her feelings. Now, although there are thousands of emotions, I ask you to start this self-examination by paring them down to the basic five.

THE BASIC FEELINGS

After discovery, it is important to allow the partner to express her feelings, her thoughts, and her beliefs. While you do not have much recovery under your belt, you nevertheless need to be a container for her feelings. This means that when she shouts at you, cries, or expresses her deepest hurt, you must be able to acknowledge those feelings and accept 100% responsibility for them. What we know to be true is that although the partner is solely responsible for her feelings and what she does with them, you can expedite the process of working through them if you validate and accept responsibility for causing the situation that created her overwhelmed emotional state.

HER BRAIN

It is important that you remember the dynamics of how partner betrayal causes a trauma induced state. The trauma is so great that the pre-frontal cortex goes offline, and the betrayed partner may have difficulty navigating her thoughts, feelings, and concerns in a logical way. If you are remorseful, and you are willing to do what it takes to strengthen this relationship, it will require that you sit with her feelings and allow her exhaustive opportunities to feel them.

Sex addicts often wonder how long it will take their partners to work through their feelings. I explain to them that this was the most horrific betrayal their partner could have encountered, and therefore it can take months or years for her to work through them. I then remind them that it will take 3-5 years for the sex addict's brain to heal from their sexually addictive behaviors and to create new neurocircuitry that supports health-ier choices. It can take just as long for the partner to fully heal from the activated trauma in her brain or the activation that is occurring as a result of her trauma. That doesn't mean she will no longer be triggered, but it does mean that she will know how to manage the triggers. Especially with your help.

> WHEN BOTH PARTIES WANT TO STAY TOGETHER, THEY SUPPORT EACH OTHER
>
> IN GETTING HEALTHIER.

When a partner is on overload, it can be helpful to share your feelings while obtaining hers. Sex addicts have difficulty figuring out how they feel, so it can be helpful to identify one of the "primary feelings."

Identifying the primary feeling can help you to understand what is going on with you and your wife so that you can form a better connection and understanding.

I commonly ask addicts to identify situations in their lives. To simplify the task, I encourage them to reduce their emotions to The Five Basic Feelings:

- Anger

- Sadness

- Happiness

- Fear

- Loneliness

If you have trouble remembering the feelings initially, I would encourage you to use the kid version:

- Mad

- Sad

- Glad

- Afraid

- Lonely

Since the first three rhyme, kids (and addicts) can easily remember the "famous five feelings." Any emotion can be reduced to any of these feelings.

Think of an umbrella with five ribs. Each rib represents one of the primary feelings. If you are feeling "frustrated" you may need to determine whether that falls under the "Anger" rib or the "Sad" rib. Pick the predominant feeling.

Oftentimes you may feel several feelings at once. When this occurs, pick the predominant one—the strongest feeling you are having in the moment. (There is a caveat that seems to be gender related. Women typically feel sadness when the real feeling is anger. Men typically report anger when the uncomfortable feeling is generally fear or sadness. Be aware of this and dig deep to determine the predominant feeling.)

HAPPINESS/SADNESS

ANGER

LONELINESS

FEAR

SERENE

GOOD

JOYFUL

EXCITED

EXUBERANT

RESENTFUL

FRUSTRATED

IRRITATED

ANNOYED

different

snubbed

less than

alone

isolated

FEARFUL

ANXIOUS

WORRIED

SCARED

UNSURE

CRESTFALLEN

SHAMED

DISCOURAGED

HURT

UPSET

SCARED

UNSURE

ANXIOUS

FEARFUL

WORRIED

FEAR

FEAR:

FEAR is a primary feeling as you walk the journey of addiction and addiction recovery. It has many faces and shows up as anxiety, worry, scaredness, and insecurity. It keeps you in a perpetual state of unrest. You question everything in your past. It consumes your belief about the future. Most importantly, it robs you from living in the moment. It is important to practice techniques that will assist you in managing fear so that you can live from a place of confidence. You need to know that the important work that you are doing to help your spouse heal will entail periods of fear. You must own the conviction that you can move through periods of fear. By doing so, you will get to the other side of relational repair.

RESENTFUL

FRUSTRATED

ANNOYED

IRRITATED

ANGER

ANGER:

Anger is a healthy emotion if you use it productively. Anger can motivate you to change yourself and your environment. It is not uncommon to feel plenty of self-loathing and anger, both in active addiction and in the beginning stages of addiction recovery. As you develop true empathy, you will get in touch with the pain you have caused your wife; this results in feeling anger towards yourself. It can be helpful to recognize the many forms of anger so that you can learn how to manage them. Frustration, annoyance, and irritation are common by-products of anger and will need to be addressed so that they don't interfere with your goal of healing. Journaling your feelings can help you externalize anger in its numerous forms so that you can process and surrender them. This will allow you to make better decisions.

ALONE.

ISOLATED.

DIFFERENT

SNUBBED

LONELINESS

LESS THAN

LONELINESS

When you were in active addiction, you were isolated and separated from the person that you wanted to be. You hid your addiction; there was no real connection. Now that you have shared your truth and you are actively working on repairing your relationship, you will again feel loneliness because your wife is going to initially fear and reject the idea that she can actually count on you. She will be afraid to trust your sincere efforts to help her heal. This is natural and will require that you identify the isolation and rejection that you feel. You will need to find ways to reassure yourself that this is a natural byproduct of the hurt and the pain that you have caused and that these feelings will be replaced with connection and trust once you work through the recovery process.

SADNESS:

SADNESS is a normal emotion, but it can leave you immobilized to take action. You will experience much sadness on your journey of recovery. Perhaps the greatest sadness you will experience is watching your wife reel from the inherent devastation of sexual betrayal. It will feel overwhelming to manage both your feelings and her feelings simultaneously. This can easily result in discouragement. It will be imperative that you don't let sadness, shame and discouragement prevent you from moving forward on your recovery journey. Sadness requires that you acknowledge the feeling and then create a helpful affirmation to move you forward towards a healthy relationship. Using an affirmation like, "I can see the devastation on her face right now, but I know I am capable of showing her my true self in recovery" can neutralize the sadness and keep you proactive in your relational recovery. Don't let sadness and discouragement stop you from doing the next right thing!

EXCITED

GOOD

EXHUBERENT

JOYFUL

SERENE

HAPPINESS

ENTHUSED

HAPPINESS

Dealing with betrayal trauma can feel exhausting. Recognizing the many facets of happiness will help to counteract the difficult feelings that you encounter as you heal. As you can see, happiness takes many forms and honoring them allows you to feel more hopeful about the recovery process. As you walk through your day, watch for the small things that contribute towards feelings of enthusiasm, serenity, excitement, and joyfulness. Your experiences may include petting your puppy, taking a walk on a sunny day, hugging your children, or reaching out to one of your fellowship buddies. Don't take happiness for granted. You must regularly acknowledge happiness to find balance in your day!

THE FIVE PRIMARY FEELINGS EXERCISE

Is there an area where you feel personally stuck? Take a few moments and think of a situation that is problematic.

- What situation causes you to feel blocked by your feelings?

  _____

  _____

  _____

- Which feeling is primarily generated when you think of this situation? (One of the five primary feelings)

  _____

- What might you do to work through that feeling?

  _____

  _____

  _____

TOOLS TO ASSIST YOU IN UNDERSTANDING AND PROCESSING YOUR FEELINGS

It is not uncommon to feel blocked or stuck by your feelings. When this occurs, it is important to identify tools that can assist you in getting more comfortable with your feelings.

Brainstorm any conceivable tool that you can utilize to work through the feeling. Your list may include: journaling, talking to your sponsor, sharing your feelings with your wife, meditating, exercising, reading something inspirational, etc...

TOOLS THAT PROCESS FEELINGS

1.

2.

3.

4.

5.

6.

7.

8.

9.

10.

It is imperative that you know which feeling is really immobilizing you. Note that the three feelings that stop people from moving through their issues are typically anger, fear, and sadness. Once you have identified the feeling, you will be able to use it proactively to address the issue that you are struggling to manage or work through. This should allow you to experience the feelings differently. When this occurs, you will be able to process correctly what might be the healthiest way to interpret and learn from your feelings. Let's look at some examples:

You are in active recovery and you have over 120 days of sobriety. You are encouraged by your progress and feel like you are finally looking at your life and your relationship with new eyes. You finally have hope—for restoration of your relationship and liberation from your addiction.

One evening you get stuck working late and you forget to call your wife. Your phone is on silent, and as you get in the car, you see she has texted and called you eight times. She is furious and accuses you of all sorts of things. You try to reassure her, but she won't listen. You get home, and she is not speaking to you. You immediately spiral into the shame cycle; you want to give up. You say all sorts of negative things to yourself and isolate from her. It seems that you can do nothing right. This scenario can play out hundreds of times during early recovery.

The partner is afraid that she can't trust the sobriety you have achieved. She can't understand how you could have forgotten to let her know that you were going to be late. She fears that you are either cheating again or you don't care enough about her to "want to make her feel safe" by keeping in contact.

- Has this happened to you? If you put yourself in this place... how might you be affected?

  _____

  _____

  _____

- What is the primary feeling you would have in this scenario?

  _____

- How can you acknowledge it without going into shame?

  _____

  _____

  _____

- What can it teach you?

  _____

  _____

  _____

- How might you use it to move forward?

  _____

  _____

  _____

This was a situation that happened to my client James. As he examined the situation, he was able to identify that he was sad. He was sad that he had reversed the positive momentum he had with his wife. He was angry with himself for forgetting to check in. He realized that he could have prevented this from happening, and that there was much he could have done to calm her fears.

- He could have taken a picture of himself at the office or in the parking lot of his work.

- He could have video-called to prove where he was to calm her fears.

- He could have used an empathy technique to let her know that he recognized the trauma and knew his behavior had triggered her.

Later that night he journaled about his sadness and committed to setting an alarm every evening at 5 p.m. to remind himself to check in with his wife and provide her the assurance she needed that he was being honest with her. His journaling helped him recognize that he had many accountability tools he could use.

When he talked it over with his therapist, she reminded him that he wouldn't have to do this forever, but that he would have to make the special effort until he had more sexual sobriety.

Would you have been as resourceful as James and been able to come up with some alternative solutions that could have rectified a very triggering situation for the partner?

TRIGGERS MAY ALWAYS OCCUR; BUT WITH GOOD SOBRIETY, THEY WILL FADE OVER TIME.

Many men have been in this position. They aren't perfect and become caught up in a project and let time get away from them. Or they forgot their phone, had it on silent, or misplaced it for a period of time. Although mistakes can happen, it is important to avoid neglectful patterns of behavior that reinforce your wife's fear.

What might you have done if you had been in James' position?

You likely would have felt sad that you had forgotten to call and thus caused her trauma. You wouldn't be able to undo the damage, but you might write a letter reassuring her that you see the pain you have caused.

You might want to say a little prayer, asking your higher power to stand with you as you work through this crisis. You might then tell her that you will place a sticky note on your computer inscribed, "TIL" (Text If Late). This will demonstrate to her that you are going to work harder on accountability.

Can you think of 3 more "Empathy Statements" for this situation if you had been James?

1. _____

_____

2. _____

_____

3. _____

_____

QUESTIONING THE RELATIONSHIP AND YOUR OWN NEEDS

Addicts often fear that they are not strong enough to weather their wives' sadness, anger, and fear. They discourage easily and worry that they will never be able to live up to what their spouse wants. When James triggered his wife, he admitted to his therapist that he was wondering if his own recovery might not be compromised by her feelings of sorrow, anger, and hatred. He felt good about himself and his recovery, yet his progress did not seem to impact his wife at all. This brought him down immensely, demonstrating that his feelings of shame and sorrow could be activators for his own sexual addiction.

You have undoubtedly watched your wife reel from the devastation of sex addiction. You have felt horrible about yourself and have wanted to crawl into a corner and disappear. Many sex addicts explain that they incur the ordeal of her anger because they know that they "deserve it." While nobody deserves to be physically or verbally attacked, it is important to understand that this behavior can be a common reaction from betrayed partners who are suffering emotional overload and are outside of their "window of tolerance."

The window of tolerance refers to the normal state from which we operate while navigating through life. When a partner experiences a betrayal, a trauma reaction occurs that activates her and makes her feel anxious, angry, scared, or hyper-vigilant. She is operating outside her window of tolerance. Conversely, when she is triggered, she may go to that place where she shuts down, checks out, or avoids by sleeping or hibernating in her room. This too is operating outside of her window of tolerance. Either reaction shows she is wounded and deeply affected, left feeling hopeless.

When this occurs, it is important to use an approach that recognizes your feelings, vulnerabilities and fears, but equally emphasizes the importance of your healthy behaviors and choices.

Don't get discouraged!

Tell yourself that you understand that your wife is not able to trust your new and healthy behaviors, and that her skepticism will not deter you from staying the course and supporting her while maintaining your recovery. Despite the fact that she cannot trust you, you are convicted to practice the relational recovery tools that will keep you together despite her fears. Partners want to know that their husband can handle the "waves of emotions" that occur because of the trauma response and triggers.

This is the time where you can tap into your confidence and conviction that you will weather her triggers, fears and trauma responses and prove that you are the husband she can count on for the duration of her healing.

You are there to Help.Her.Heal.

Your response to her trauma:

1. Stay the course.

2. Maintain your confidence while being transparent, authentic and honest.

3. Be patient as she pushes you away because she is afraid to be hurt again.

4. By showing her that you can be a safe container that holds her fears, you will prove your reliability and love for her.

So, let's look at partner betrayal and how it causes stress reactions.

A husband has had multiple affairs, leaving his wife feeling betrayed. She feels sad and depressed and yet when she really sits and reflects, she realizes she is angry that he cheated on her, and angry that she can no longer trust him.

This is actually an instinctive survival technique. She needs to move into feeling anger instead of sadness so that she can figure out how to address the infidelity. It gives her adrenaline to start working on recovery from the betrayal. Staying stuck in the sadness would have left her lethargic, stuck in the victim role.

By getting in touch with the anger, she sets boundaries. She tells her husband what he needs to do to rebuild the partnership. She sets aside time to look at what she needs if she is going to become a single mother with children. She uses the anger to energize herself into taking better care of herself—for instance, starting to play tennis, or attending church more regularly. She joins an online group for partner betrayal, where she journals her feelings and shares them to give them a voice.

To better understand how your acting out has affected her emotionally, you must learn how to contain her feelings without going straight to shame. Remember that shame tells you that you are a bad person and you will never be able to accurately empathize with others if you are unable to regulate shame and reduce it to guilt. Guilt is having done something bad. Shame is believing that you are bad.

 SHAME

Let's look at what shaming thoughts you may be feeling and find some alternative thinking that will appropriately define the situation and assist you in moving forward into healthy recovery.

In the first column of the grid below, list ten consequences that have occurred because of your acting out. In the 2nd column, enter the shaming thoughts that ruminate in your head. In the 3rd column, write kinder, healthier thoughts that change the shame to a more reality-based thought.

COLUMN 1 CONSEQUENCES OF ACTING OUT	COLUMN 2 SHAMING THOUGHTS	COLUMN 3 RE-FRAMED THOUGHTS
Example: I have destroyed my wife's self-esteem.	I am perverted and sick.	My addiction caused me to do unthinkable things, but I am on a journey to be a better person.
1.		
2.		
3.		
4.		
5.		

COLUMN 1 CONSEQUENCES OF ACTING OUT	COLUMN 2 SHAMING THOUGHTS	COLUMN 3 RE-FRAMED THOUGHTS
6.		
7.		
8.		
9.		
10.		

Shame has its roots in the past. It is the anchor that weighs you down and makes you feel that you can't get healthy and are not worthy of being healthy. You have to actively change the way you see yourself! As you begin to notice your negative thinking, you will want to practice what we call cognitive behavioral thinking, referred to as CBT. You will want to create more realistic thoughts that reflect where you are in your recovery today. You will want to note your negative thinking and ask yourself, how is my behavior different from the old acting out behaviors, and how have I grown stronger?

Shame is what's holding you back from being the person you really want to be. When I work with addicts, I help them to recognize their cognitive distortions. The truth of the matter is that you are in recovery, and you must recognize and acknowledge your changes to move forward and to get healthier.

When you are in a relationship with your spouse, it is important to remind her that you are seeing things differently. Yet, expect that she likely won't believe it because you have lied to her so consistently in the past. She "has" to work from the premise that she "can't" trust you so that she will not be "deceived" again.

THERE WILL BE TIMES THAT THIS WILL SEEM LIKE A FUTILE EFFORT BECAUSE IT WILL FEEL THAT YOU ARE "DAMNED IF YOU DO GET HEALTHY, AND DAMNED IF YOU DON'T."

Please don't get discouraged. Time will help her to see your changes. It is important that you not return to shame when this relational interaction occurs. It can be helpful to say, "I can imagine why it is hard for you to believe anything that comes out of my mouth, and I am sorry for the pain that I have caused you."

I have worked with thousands of couples; trust me, this dynamic gets better over time. But the prerequisite is that you maintain good recovery and show her that repairing the fractured relationship is your #1 goal.

"PARTNERS DO WHAT TRAUMA SURVIVORS DO.
THEY SEEK WHAT THEY CANNOT FIND:
SAFETY IN AN UNSAFE SITUATION."

-DR. BARBARA STEFFENS, CO-AUTHOR OF
YOUR SEXUALLY ADDICTED SPOUSE: HOW PARTNERS CAN COPE AND HEAL.

CHAPTER 3
HER NEEDS

HER NEEDS—PARTNERS HAVE MANY NEEDS, BUT THEY REALLY NEED TO FIND SAFETY IN THEIR RELATIONSHIP WITH YOU.

HOW TO ASSESS HER NEEDS AND FEELINGS

It would be foolhardy to expect that you would know what your wife needs, especially after traumatizing her. Most women who have discovered sexual addiction secretly want to believe that their husband can change, but their fears take precedent over their desires. They have been so hurt and traumatized that their amygdala is keeping them protected; they are ready to go into fight or freeze mode to avoid further pain. This means that she will inherently be skeptical of sharing her needs with you. Her faith in you and the relationship is crushed. She can't take a chance at being hurt again.

This is where you need to do your due diligence and keep reminding her that as long as she has agreed to stay in the partnership, you are committed to be the husband that she deserves. This means that you are going to keep asking her what she needs. An empathy statement that you might use might look something like this:

"I know that you can't trust me to have your best interest at heart because of all the damage that I have caused. But I am here for you. I want to know what I can do to make things easier for you right now."

Or,

"I don't expect you to believe me after everything that I have put you through, but I sincerely want to know how you are feeling."

WHY IS IT SO HARD FOR YOU TO KNOW WHAT SHE NEEDS?

You are at a deficit because you are an addict, and addicts are inherently self-interested. They have to be in order to maintain the addiction. You likely have practiced dishonesty for years, and so your self-centeredness has canceled out any real chance of understanding how your addiction would affect your wife because you needed to stay in denial and continue your selfishness to maintain the addiction.

Why should you put her needs first? The men that I have worked with exponentially make progress when they recognize that they have cheated their wives out of safety and stability. Their wives thought they knew who they were married to and what their marriage consisted of, only to find that their relationship was one big lie. They have been blaming themselves for not seeing it sooner, for being so stupid. Your wife is angry at herself for trusting in you and the sanctity of marriage.

> ALTHOUGH WE TELL PARTNERS THAT IT WAS AN ADDICT'S FULL-TIME JOB TO DECEIVE THEM AND THAT PARTNERS COULD NOT HAVE KNOWN THE LEVEL OF DECEPTION IN THEIR MARRIAGE, THEY STILL SECOND DOUBT THEMSELVES AND WONDER HOW THEY COULD HAVE BEEN SO BLIND AND SO TRUSTING.

Your spouse's entire world has crumbled, and you are at the core of that pain. So, it is important for you to put her needs first and show her that you are going to do it differently. The challenging aspect of this is that you likely don't know what her needs are, and so I am going to guide you and encourage you to find out what she needs. And I assure you, sometimes there will be requests that you didn't see coming.

SEXUAL ADDICTION IS A RELATIONAL ISSUE AND REQUIRES TREATMENT FOR THE RELATIONSHIP

IT REQUIRES A NEW PHILOSOPHY

You may have been taught that your recovery work is solely your own and your wife should not be privy to your work. However, sexual addiction is a relational disorder and so that thinking is old-school; it does nothing to help her healing. It is true that she should not direct your recovery but keeping her informed of your progress is paramount to her feeling safe and that is your responsibility (unless she would prefer that you keep your progress to yourself).

LET ME REPEAT: YOUR WIFE WILL NEED TO KNOW ABOUT THE DETAILS OF YOUR RECOVERY TO IMPROVE HER SENSE OF SECURITY, AND SO THAT SHE CAN FEEL SAFE.

I have worked with thousands of partners, and I have never met a partner who wanted the addict to keep his progress or struggles to himself. I have met women who would prefer to hear "deal breaking" struggles and are totally comfortable with you working with your support system informing them of the smaller struggles. But in general, having empathy is asking her what she needs so that you work on your honesty and transparency.

WHAT DO YOU THINK YOUR WIFE NEEDS?

In the boxes provided, put together some ideas that may contribute to her needs. When you are done with the exercise, make sure to ask her what you can do to meet her needs, whether its safety, communication, or other areas. She may have things to add to a list or other needs to include.

MY WIFE NEEDS... TO FEEL SAFE

What can I do to make my wife feel safe?

- Allow her to track my whereabouts.

- Take pictures of my location.

- Check in with her 4 times a day.

- Allow her to see all my devices.

- Take regular polygraph tests.

Now list 3 things that you can do for her:

1.

2.

3.

Feedback / Notes:

MY WIFE NEEDS...MORE COMMUNICATION

What can I do to improve my communication?

- Have regular check ins nightly.

- Share with her when I have struggles.

- Share with her my fears.

Now list 3 things that you can do for her:

1.

2.

3.

Feedback / Notes:

MY WIFE NEEDS... *TO KNOW ABOUT MY RECOVERY*

How can I share with her what I am doing to stay in good recovery?

- I contacted my sponsor today.

- I completed my *Out of the Shadows* reading.

- I decided to read a partner-sensitive book, so I picked up *Intimate Deceptions* by Dr. Sheri Keffer PhD.

Now list 3 things that you can do for her:

1.

2.

3.

Feedback / Notes:

MY WIFE NEEDS... *TO KNOW THAT I LOVE HER,*

AND THAT SHE IS THE MOST IMPORTANT PERSON IN THE WORLD TO ME.

How do I show her that I have realigned with what really matters and that I want her and our marriage to be the focus of my life?

- Spend time together.

- Give her small gifts to remind her of how special she is.

- Do things for her.

- Take care of the kids and give her a night off.

- Share my appreciation of her.

Now list 3 things that you can do for her:

1.

2.

3.

Feedback / Notes:

MY WIFE NEEDS... _____

What can I do to meet my wife's needs?

-

-

-

Now list 3 things that you can do for her:

1.

2.

3.

Feedback / Notes:

MY WIFE NEEDS... _____

What can I do to meet my wife's needs?

-
-
-

Now list 3 things that you can do for her:

1.

2.

3.

Feedback / Notes:

Checking in with your wife to determine her needs will send her consistent messages that you care about her safety. Safety is a primary need a partner has to recalibrate and renegotiate the new relationship in recovery.

Your wife will likely need you to display recovery behaviors that minimize her triggers, and that is why it is so important to help her manage them.

CHAPTER 4
TRIGGERS

TRIGGERS

In working with thousands of partners, it has become apparent that all a spouse wants to do is to feel safe again. Whether she felt like she had a good marriage or she knew that the relationship had problems, she had no idea that you were living a dual life that entailed lies, deception and secrecy. As a result, this trauma has deeply affected her brain, and her brain has gone into overdrive. This information has likely impacted the amygdala which lies at the bottom of the brain above the brainstem. This part of the brain stores and processes information, and its main function is to keep your spouse safe. Therefore, it guides your wife to react to her pain, anxiety, and anger by going into *fight*, *flight*, or *freeze* mode. If the protective mechanism moves her towards *fight*, she will likely go into "attack mode." She will say mean and hurtful things. She may become physically aggressive, pushing, shoving and hitting you as her emotions intensify. Many wives tell me that they are reacting to their emotions in ways that they could never have conceived. They wonder if they are going crazy because they have never in the past resorted to name calling or aggressive behavior. It will be important for you to have clear boundaries because it is never acceptable for your wife to physically aggress against you.

It is important that you understand what happens when your wife is triggered so that you can empathize with her and spend time using empathy exercises or trigger busters to help ground her so that she can move through the trigger.

It is important for you to remember the following:

TRIGGERS MAY HAVE ORIGINS THAT YOU BOTH CAN TRACE.

Perhaps you came home and told her that you saw an old affair partner at the drugstore. Maybe you and your partner drove by a hotel or massage parlor where you had previously acted out. She may become triggered by the ding of a text on your tablet. She might be aware of an anniversary date of her first discovery. In other words, there may be an actual connection to a person, place, or thing that triggers your spouse.

TRIGGERS MAY OCCUR WITHOUT ANY DIRECT LINK TO A SITUATION THAT IS ASSOCIATED WITH YOUR ACTING OUT.

What we know about trauma is that there can be associations to the trigger that are unconscious. Many times, triggers are stored with the 5 senses of experience. People perceive the world through their sight, smell, taste, touch or sound. For some partners, they may have been in a yellow kitchen when they saw the text from a prostitute arranging a "hook-up" and so when the partner enters a yellow room, unbeknownst to her, she has a trauma response that feels uncontrollable and frightening. She has no idea what is happening to her and has no association to the yellow room which is actively triggering her unconsciously.

YOUR PARTNER DOES NOT NECESSARILY KNOW WHY SHE IS BEING TRIGGERED.

Can you imagine how scary that would be to not know why your brain has gone offline? One minute your partner is going through her normal day and then BAM—the sound of a text coming in, the color of the yellow walls, a smell that she associates with the moment of discovery occurs and she is thrown back into post-traumatic stress. She has to navigate through the fear, panic, and fright that accompanies the association.

Christina Bell has a wonderful chart that helps you to understand what happens to your wife when she is triggered. You can visit her site at www. ChristinaBell.net to access her tools for working through triggers.

MANAGING TRIGGERS

BACKGROUND FACTORS
(Ever Present)
- Past Betrayals
- Past Trauma
- Current Stressors

1. THE TRIGGER

- Partner Inconsistency
- Ambiguous Situation
- Broken Promise
- Media / Outside Influence

5. OVER TIME, THE COUPLE AVOIDS TALKING ABOUT ISSUES

- To Avoid Conflict
- Greater Distance
- Resentments Can Fuel Acting out

4. ESCALATION OF CONFLICT
(Partner Hurt)

REMEMBER: TRIGGERS ARE A NATURAL PART OF RECOVERY. MANAGING TRIGGERS AS A TEAM PROVIDES AN OPPORTUNITY TO BUILD TRUST.

OF BETRAYAL[1]

2. "ALARM / BOMB" GOES OFF (Partner Hurt)

- Physiological Flooding
- Preoccupation

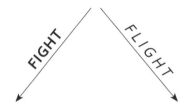

FIGHT

- Reactive Anger
- Checking / Policing
- Questions
- All or Nothing Thinking
- "Kitchen Sinking"

FLIGHT

- Avoidance
- "Stuffing" Concerns

BETRAYING PARTNER TASKS:

- Provide Comfort and Reassurance to Spouse
- Work on Reliability and Thoughtfulness
- Initiate Repair Attempts
- Volunteer Information About Thoughts and Feelings

3. BETRAYING PARTNER IS OVER-WHELMED BY INTENSITY / REACTION

Defends / Minimizes   Shuts Down / Avoids

BETRAYED PARTNER TASKS:

- Self-care
- Emotional Regulation
- Expressing Needs Moderately

[1]Managing Triggers of Betrayal Chart by Christina Bell. Adapted for use with permission from author. ChristinaBell.net © July 2017

So as your wife heals, she will need you to be patient as she experiences the frustration, sadness and anxiety that accompanies the triggers. She will likely remind you that she is going through this "Hell" because of your acting out.

An addict who is not in good recovery will either lash out or go into isolation to avoid feeling the shame that normally accompanies her anger/fears. As Christina Bell exemplifies on her diagram, it is important to deal with the triggers as a team, and when you assist your wife in working through the triggers, you are helping to build trust. You will need to provide comfort and reassurance to your spouse. Of course, the first step is to have good recovery so that she can begin to trust that you have changed. Then you need good reliability.

- This is why you have to be predictable and put her first.

- You have to be reliable by letting her know when you are leaving and coming home. You will need to follow through with promises and commitments.

- You can help her out by taking over with the household duties and the kids. You will need to step up and provide a true team approach to your family.

When she experiences a trigger, you will need to acknowledge exactly what you are noticing in the here and now. Christina believes that it is helpful to provide repair attempts, which John Gottman defined as partner requests. In his book *The Seven Principles for Making Marriage Work*, Gottman defines a repair attempt as any statement or action—verbal, physical or otherwise—meant to diffuse negativity and keep a conflict from escalating out of control. Dr. Gottman calls repair attempts a secret weapon of emotionally intelligent couples.

When an infraction has occurred, it is helpful to ask your spouse "What can I do for you right now?" or "What do you need?" Maybe she needs more space, or perhaps she needs you to hold her. Maybe she needs you to sit with her in silence as she goes through the trigger.

Unfortunately, many therapists do not know how to advise you to help your wife. They do not know how to help you to help her work through her triggers which leaves you feeling inadequate, insecure, fearful and shamed.

You can assist her in getting through this! But it takes ample practice and patience for yourself and your partner. Remember that she is in full blown trauma when she experiences triggers and wants safety and stabilization.

Dorit Reichental and Janice Caudill have come up with a Trigger Busters' protocol which can help you and your partner work through the triggers together. They have broken it down into 4 stages whereby you initially:

1. First calm yourself, so that your voice, tone, and demeanor are comforting and soothing. Then, identify what you believe that you are noticing with your partner in the here and now. You then ask, "Are you triggered?" You then validate what you are seeing which in most cases is the trigger. "It makes sense to me that you would be triggered," or if you are confused about the trigger, simply "I can see that you are triggered."

2. Help her to stay grounded and in the here and now by orienting her to the present. Remind her that she is safe and nothing bad is happening now.

3. De-escalate the experience by saying something nurturing and safe. "I am not doing anything now that would put you in harm's way. This is a bad trigger, and I imagine it is reminding you of my past acting. I am not acting out now, you are safe, and I am right here with you." If your spouse is open to comforting touch, place your hand on her back.

4. Once the trigger is defused, your partner will be able to anchor onto your regulated nervous system and come fully into the present moment to re-engage and reconnect with you. We call this co-regulation. You have gone through the Trigger Busters' cycle together!

On the next page is Dorit's and Janice's "cheat sheet" for what they call *Relational CPR for Sexual Addiction and Triggers.*

TRIGGER BUSTERS: RELATIONAL CPR
(4 Steps to Safety & Co-Regulation)

TRIGGER ACTIVATION

Partner: left brain goes offline, right brain takes over as she becomes triggered. Addict must *actively* help the partner calm her nervous system.

IDENTITY THE TRIGGER

Clarification: Clarify if spouse is triggered.
   "I can see X, Y, Z. Are you triggered?"

Accountability: *Do Not* defend, blame, shame, minimize, invalidate, judge, criticize, debate, stonewall, correct with irrelevant detail, withdraw, escape, or project anger.

Validation: As soon as addict realizes that partner is triggered, s/he *validates* partner.
"*I can see how scared and unsafe you are, it must remind you of... It makes sense to me that you feel triggered, scared, angry, unsafe, etc.*"

ORIENT TO HERE AND NOW

Addict gently reminds the partner that s/he is safe, and nothing bad is happening right now: (triggered partner cannot differentiate between past and present)

   "I am not doing anything now to put you at risk or in danger; it's a bad trigger—that happened when I was acting out.

I am not acting out now, you are safe, and I am right here with you, I have your back."

STEP 3 DE-ESCALATION, SAFETY, & STABILIZATION USING TRIGGER BUSTERS

What does the nurturing/protective addict need to continue saying and doing to help the partner down-regulate? (Addict may need to reassure and repeat the message multiple times)

As the hijacked brain comes back online, the addict emphatically attunes to the partner and states:

"I can see this was a really bad trigger. You are safe right now. I have your back."

STEP 4 SOCIAL ENGAGEMENT

Notice the somatic, felt sense signs that the trigger is being defused. For example, the partner's eyes, voice, and face may soften as the body begins to relax and breathing regulates. *Now the two of you can have a real conversation. In fact, your partner may even want to connect with you.*

SHE IS NOT GETTING BETTER

Jill came in with her husband after they were seeing a marital therapist who was smart enough to know that this case was more complicated than he had worked in the past, and required a sexual addiction specialist or partner sensitive therapist to assist the coupleship.

Prior to discovery, Jill had no idea that her husband, Tom, was acting out at work. Despite the fact that she sensed that something was wrong, she never could have imagined that he was having affairs at work, had groomed her friends in the neighborhood, had approached one of his son's teachers at school and even had made overtures to her sister!

Jill's life was contaminated. Every aspect of her life had been impacted and she could no longer take walks in the community, go to the store, or even visit her son's school without wondering who might know of her husband's indiscretions. As a result of this contamination, she became more and more activated. She resented that he had ruined her sense of safety and literally affected all areas of her life. She no longer felt safe, and did not know how she could ever feel normal again. These feelings turned into contempt for him. Every time she looked at him or he entered their home, she would snarl and jab him emotionally.

Although Tom could understand her anger and he believed that he deserved her outbursts, he also wondered why she was not noticing his changes. She did not seem happy that he had gone through a disclosure weekend with a professional and had purged his soul to get all of his secrets out. He felt so much better, but his wife was not seeing the growth. He began to wonder if she would be better off without him. He had caused her such great sorrow, and she seemed absolutely miserable by his presence.

He also admitted to his therapist that he was wondering if his own recovery might not be compromised by her deep feelings of sorrow, anger, and hatred. He felt so good about himself, and his progress did not seem to impact his wife at all. This brought him down immensely. He knew that his feelings of shame and sorrow could be activators for his own sexual addiction recovery.

THE MANY COMPARTMENTS OF AN ADDICT

The therapist encouraged him to compartmentalize his feelings. He had done this for so long while he was actively involved in sexual addiction. He, like so many other addicts, would put his family in one compartment, his work in another, and his civic duties in another, all while he acted out. He had so many different compartments for the many lives he led. Therefore, his therapist told him that he would be a pro at being able to put his sadness and shame in a compartment and instead use his good recovery, so that he could be there for his wife.

What he knew to be true was that he was going to be instrumental in helping his wife's recovery, but this meant that he accepted the fact that he spent years and years deceiving her, and now he needed to sit with her as she worked out her feelings of betrayal and rejection.

The therapist also explained that not only was his wife in the *fight* phase of *fight, flight,* or *freeze,* but that those strong feelings to attack, to be angry, and to hurt him were really a result of the rejection she felt. As you remember, as the amygdala is activated in the brain, the feelings are transported to the prefrontal cortex, but they first must visit the anterior cingulate cortex and anterior insular cortex. This part of the brain, which is about the size of a nutshell, holds the emotional capacity and is especially sensitive to rejection. Whenever a partner experiences betrayal, whether she is feeling anger, sadness, loneliness, or fear, her sense of rejection is deeply compromised, and she looks for ways to protect herself.

As a result, the therapist helped him to understand that he was not only "righting the wrongs" by sitting with her for as long as it would take to make things better, but he was also repairing the fractured relationship by withstanding the barbs, the jabs, and the hurt she felt. Under normal circumstances, a therapist would help a client assert himself and stand up for himself to teach his wife that she cannot be verbally aggressive against him. However, in the world of sexual betrayal and trauma, the therapist needs to help the addict contain his feelings by not reacting to that verbal *fight* part of the amygdala. This means he may need to be patient for 6 to 18 months while she works on emotional regulation with her therapist so that she can return to a better window of tolerance. The therapist taught him how to use visual imagery like Teflon—an imaginary force field that protects him from internalizing her anger and feeling self-loathing.

I'm sure as you have watched your wife reel from the devastation of sex addiction, you have felt horrible about yourself and wanted to crawl into a corner and disappear. Many of the sex addicts that I work with explain that they incur the ordeal of her anger, because they know "that they deserve it." Although nobody deserves to be physically or verbally attacked, it can be a common reaction from betrayed partners who are in emotional overload and are outside the window of tolerance.

The important thing is to "hang in there" and be the container for her feelings. You can help her to recover from the betrayal, but you have to commit to the process! I would encourage you to find some sex addicts who are in great recovery and who are partner sensitive. Not only will they help you through your pain and shame, they will remind you that this is a natural consequence to partner betrayal, and they will encourage you to stay with being empathetic.

True empathy takes skill, patience and a commitment to putting your betrayed partner first to restore the relationship. When you practice empathy, you will be letting her know that you get her pain, and you are ready to do what it takes to help her process it. But what is empathy? How do you learn to put someone first when you have been involved in a compulsion that required you to put yourself first? In the following chapter, you will learn about empathy and how to practice it to create trust to repair and restore the relationship and to have closeness that the addiction stole from both of you!

CHAPTER 5
EMPATHY
THE BUILDING BLOCK OF TRUST

EMPATHY, THE BUILDING BLOCK OF TRUST

A common response I hear from sex addicts is, "I have tried to use empathy, but she doesn't trust it."

Learning the new skill of empathy would be easier to practice if your partner believed you and accepted it easily, but the truth of the matter is that you need to learn the skill to build connection so that she can begin to trust you again. And it is a natural process that she will reject initially because she can't believe that you are seeing things from her perspective. Her trauma response is initially involuntary and requires that you continue to address her pain by seeing it through her eyes.

YOUR SEXUAL ADDICTION AND THE BRAIN

There are two types of patterns we see when assessing the etiology of sex addiction. Some children, early in their development, were involved in some type of sexual behavior that caused them pain, shame, curiosity, or intrigue. As they got older, they looked for other opportunities to act out the behaviors and/or feelings. This resulted in something we call sexual trauma reenactment and can be the precursor for acting out in adulthood. If you were involved in sex play as a child and you felt both excited and guilty about it, you may have developed a compulsion behaviorally to act out similar events or feelings as an adult. Perhaps there was something pleasurable and guilt provoking in sexually acting out with prostitutes and this became a compulsion that became uncontrollable. This caused your brain to develop neurocircuitry that would require ongoing compulsive behavior to maintain its existence. Your sex addiction became a brain disorder and part of the healing requires new neurocircuitry to occur that replaces the old.

The second reason for sexually addictive behaviors to occur is due to the development of compulsive, habitual behaviors that become routinized and obsessive. There have been many sex addicts that experienced no trauma in their childhood but started using porn periodically. This behavior increased in frequency and intensity and resulted in the addict no longer being able to control his acting out.

Most addicts describe the compulsion as wanting to know "what else was out there" that they had not seen before. The addiction was about the intrigue of what they might have missed.

EMPATHY: A WINDOW TO HER PAIN

Empathy is a skill you need regardless of whether this relationship survives the infidelity. Part of your job is now to make a living amends to your partner to show her that you are going to be a man of integrity and be the man that she deserves and desires. The living amends that you will make to her cannot occur unless empathy is at the heart of it. Developing empathy allows you to feel good about yourself and restores your integrity. Empathy will show her that you understand her fears!

> TRUE SEXUAL ADDICTION RECOVERY DEPENDS ON YOUR ABILITY TO LEARN
>
> SENSITIVITY AND EMPATHY.

Sex addicts will say "We didn't communicate prior to the discovery, and we really aren't communicating now that she knows about my indiscretions." Empathy can be used in those situations too. Empathy is a form of communication and shows your partner that you heard what she is saying, and you are noticing the collateral damage. You want to support her by being accountable for the pain you caused. In your Triggers Chapter, you learned about Trigger Busters techniques that showed her a deep level of empathy. Your sexual addiction has created a lot of guilt and shame and when you feel your partner start to reject, criticize, or mistrust you, you may want to revert to the old style of communication whereby you get defensive, want to check out, give up or fight back. When you make the conscious choice to use empathy, it can defuse her angry feelings and your protective stance.

Therapists know that problems in a marriage are never the result of "just one person" and yet it is extremely important that you remember that "ANY" problems that you had in your relationship are now secondary to the damage that was caused as a result of you sexually acting out. You must take full responsibility for the betrayal and consistently show empathy before you can attend to the other normal marital issues that were there prior to the discovery.

REMEMBER, YOU NEVER WANT TO SEND HER THE MESSAGE THAT YOUR PREVIOUS PROBLEMS PRIOR TO DISCOVERY CAUSED YOUR ACTING OUT.

In other words, you will not be able to get to the inherent problems in your marriage until you "right the wrongs" in regard to your acting out.

This process requires that you show up and develop the skills to right those wrongs, rebuild the trust, reassure her that you are new and improved, and consequently, take your marriage to the next level.

Can you imagine how incredible the marriage would have been if you had learned empathy, healthier communication, and true connection? Can you imagine what it will be like to build a sacred space to give and receive the love that you always wanted? I have seen couples achieve this and be able to have the relationship they have always wanted. But they first learned the skills for connection and trust. It is up to you to get the process started!

SKILLS THAT BUILD EMPATHY: REFLECTIVE LISTENING AND FOCUSED LISTENING©

ONE OF THE BEST WAYS TO COMMUNICATE IS TO LISTEN.

They say that one of the best ways to communicate is to listen. When you are listening to your spouse, you are actively working on processing what she is saying so that you will understand her better. Marital therapists know that "focused listening" can be terribly difficult because it involves listening without wanting to explain or defend your point of view. This is hard for any coupleship, but it is especially difficult for couples who are dealing with relationship betrayal because there is so much emotion that naturally occurs that it is normal to want to explain the pain that is occurring behind the scenes. Therefore, it can be helpful to practice a technique that ensures that you are both really listening to each other.

REFLECTIVE LISTENING

One of the simplest tools to improve communication is a strategy developed by Carl Rogers called "Reflective Listening." It is a communication strategy involving two key steps: seeking to understand a person's idea and then offering the idea back to the person to confirm the idea has been understood correctly. Empathy is at the center of Roger's approach.

When working with a betrayed partner, reflective listening is when you listen to your partner with the sole "soul" purpose of understanding and hearing what she has to say. You are working on conveying to her that you heard her. It does not require that you totally understand or agree with her, but you are generally interested in her point of view.

FOCUSED LISTENING©

Focused Listening© requires that you follow the protocol below to attend to your wife's facial gestures, body posture and other non-verbals.

I would encourage you to use it during your check in each night. This process works best if you:

- Face each other.

- Look directly into each other's eyes.

- Keep the topic to 3 minutes or less.

- You repeat back her words only. In other words, you repeat back exactly what she has said without editorializing or summarizing.

- You finalize the session by asking, "Did I get that right?"

She then has an opportunity to say yes or clarify what she said so that you can repeat the process until you get it right.

Although this may seem frustrating at first, the process allows you to show her that you care about her thoughts and feelings. It also gives her an opportunity to have a voice. It diffuses conflict, because the process requires an intense amount of focus on what you see and hear. She knows that you will not dispute or interrupt her. Part of the healing process involves your spouse being able to share her overwhelming feelings about the betrayal. She will forever wonder if you understand the gravity of what you did to her and want to express the pain. This may seem like a lifelong sentence for both of you, but the good news is that over time you both deepen your desire for intimacy and so you can develop a strong bond of love and connection...but it does take time!

As you use Focused Listening© and repeat what you heard, you can decide together how to negotiate that into your daily lives.

THIS MAY SEEM LIKE A LIFELONG SENTENCE FOR BOTH OF YOU, BUT THE GOOD NEWS IS THAT OVER TIME, YOU BOTH DEEPEN YOUR DESIRE FOR INTIMACY AND SO YOU CAN DEVELOP A STRONG BOND OF LOVE AND CONNECTION.

NEGOTIATION AND COMPROMISE

Marital theorists and therapists know that negotiation and compromise is at the cornerstone of making a marriage work smoothly. Initially after partner betrayal, it will likely be necessary to give her more opportunities to feel like she has some control in the situation. That is why you have so diligently listed (in Chapter 1) what her needs are because you will be looking for ways to show her that your priority is making sure those needs get met. As the relationship gets healthier and trust is rebuilt, you will be renegotiating what you both can do to ensure that both of you are getting your needs met in healthy ways. If you think back to your relationship in the beginning, you may have had a more equal relationship where you both were checking in with each other to assess how each of you were doing regarding the relationship. The relationship seemed equal in that both of you wanted to help each other get the coupleship's needs met.

After the betrayal occurred, your spouse's entire world has been shattered and everything that she ever knew has seemed to disappear after discovery. You have the capability of giving her a sense of security again, but this requires that you make her top priority and reassure her that she will get to make decisions that affect her safety. The power differential has been affected by your acting out and now it is time to "temporarily" show her that her wants and needs will come first. Therefore, she will need to let you know what will help her feel safe again.

Your ability to compromise and negotiate will need to take a backseat to her need to know that you really want to stay together, and that you will do whatever it takes to make her feel secure again. This power differential is only temporary until you prove that you understand what it takes to make things right. She may have a list of things that she needs to work back into trusting you.

With many of the couples we work with, the list might look like:

- *PHYSICAL SAFETY:* Your spouse may need more closeness or distance to show her that you are willing to attend to her needs.

  » I need us to sleep apart for a while until I can feel good about us being in bed together.

  » I need you to stay in a hotel the next time you slip and do not let me know in the 24-hour agreement contract that we have.

- *EMOTIONAL SAFETY:* This may require that you go the extra steps to provide her emotional safety in regard to your previous acting out.

  » I need you to find another job since you had over 7 affair partners at work and I can't stop ruminating about the chances that you will slip and your "drug" (women) will be right down the hall from you.

  » I need us to move since you groomed, flirted and slept with many of the women in the neighborhood, and I can't tolerate wondering who knows and who doesn't know.

  » I need you to tell your parents what you did so that they won't villainize me for being angry and sad all the time.

  » I need you to tell our kids so that they know why Mom is "checked out."

- *RECOVERY SAFETY:* Normally with addiction, the spouse would not be so instrumental in helping an addict design his recovery program to make her feel safe, but since this addiction has dramatically affected the reality of the spouse, it will be necessary to co-create a recovery program that shows her that you are 100% invested in getting healthy. You will be seeking the tools you need to ensure abstinence and insure her safety!

> » I need you to participate in Carol's recovery tools so that I am seeing you actively work a recovery program.

> » I need you to go to 3 meetings a week so that I know that you are in a healthy environment.

> » I need you to go to men's meetings only and NOT to go to co-ed meetings. It makes no sense to me why you think I would allow you to go to meetings with female sex addicts.

NOTE: Now the truth of the matter is that female sex addicts in recovery are not a threat to male sex addicts in recovery, but you broke that bond of safety so are doing what it takes to make her feel safe and to help her feel less activated.

- *SPIRITUAL SAFETY*: The partner may need to incorporate other support systems to increase her sense of spiritual safety.

> » I need us to start going to church again.

> » I need you to go to synagogue with me.

> » I need us to go to a church where the pastor understands that I was not at fault for this travesty in our relationship.

> » I need us to go to a new church where everyone does not know what happened to us.

> » I need us to go to a small group.

> » I need you to tell the pastor what you are struggling with and ask for his prayers.

DOING WHATEVER IT TAKES

It is my experience that the addicts that want to rebuild their relationship with their wives want to do whatever it takes to make that happen. It will not always be like this, but just in the same way that you are working on rebuilding your own character with recovery tools that are greatly enhancing your life, you are also allowing your relationship to be restored in ways that will assure your wife that you are being honest, transparent and authentic.

IT MAY SEEM LIKE YOUR WIFE HAS ALL THE CONTROL, BUT I ASSURE YOU THAT YOUR RELATIONSHIP WILL BECOME MUTUAL ONCE THE SAFETY HAS BEEN ESTABLISHED, AND ONCE YOUR RECOVERY IS WELL ESTABLISHED!

CHECKING IN WITH HER NEEDS

Ask your spouse what she needs to feel safe in this relationship. In the first chapter, you identified her needs. Ask her what you could do that would help to restore the relationship to move on.

List her responses here:

1. _____

_____

2. _____

_____

3. _____

_____

4. _____

_____

5. _____

_____

6. _____

_____

7. _____

_____

8. _____

_____

9. _____

_____

10. _____

_____

When you address these needs, you are showing her that you have empathy for the pain that you caused, and she will feel validated by your efforts. Attending to her needs using empathy, reflective listening, and focused listening also strengthens your communication and suggests that you want to know how she feels and what she thinks.

Another opportunity to develop empathy is to use a process that reinforces your ability to understand how she must feel after the wake of discovery and disclosure. Many men are not quite sure how to communicate in a way that lets her know that he sees her pain and so AVR will help break down the process so that you can check your steps and know that you are right there with both her and her pain.

EMPATHY: RECOGNIZING THE PAIN YOUR ACTIONS HAVE CAUSED HER

THE AVR FORMULA©

Partners consistently tell me that they want the addict to understand the depths and devastation of their pain. Although the addict is living with the pain that they have caused daily, part of the partners healing process is to be reminded that her husband sees the pain and can link it back to the reason for the pain. *This process must happen consistently for her to feel safe enough to trust the recovery process.* She wants to believe that you, her husband, will never do this again, but she has no guarantee. Her heart wants to trust you, but her head and experience is telling her it is not safe to be this vulnerable, so she keeps her guard up and looks for reasons to reject your attempts at honesty and authenticity. This is going to require that you consistently practice empathy in all sorts of ways.

Using AVR assures her that you are linking up your previous actions to her feelings. It also reminds her of what you are going to do to rebuild her foundation of safety.

Often in therapy, the addict needs a formula to help him respond to his spouse in a way that shows her that he realizes the damage that he has caused and how his sexual addiction has affected her.

We have been trained to know that the quickest way that an addict can redeem himself and prove to his spouse that he will do whatever it takes to build the trust back is to recognize the pain and remind her that he knows he caused it. It is then important for him to validate her feelings and make sure he can assess her feelings appropriately and then to reassure her that he will do whatever it takes to rebuild the confidence she once had in him.

THE AVR FORMULA©

- **ACKNOWLEDGING** *THE ISSUE*: Practicing AVR requires that you acknowledge the situation and accompanying pain.

- **VALIDATION** *OF HER FEELINGS USING THE FIVE PRIMARY FEELINGS*: I can see as you discuss that issue that you feel (Anger, Sadness, Loneliness, Happiness or Fear.)

- **REASSURANCE** *THAT YOU WILL HELP HER HEAL*: I want you to know that I am working on my recovery skills, and I never want to go back to that old addict behavior again.

MARK AND SANDRA'S STORY

Mark was a practicing pediatrician and had agreed to do three 1-month mission trips to Haiti. After the 2nd year of mission work, he began to act out in isolation while he was away on his trips. He had always felt he was bi-sexual but had never acted on it, but being so far away from home allowed him to spend hundreds of hours on the INTERNET looking at gay porn and searching sites that connected him to gay and bi-sexual men.

When he came home, his addiction escalated, and he started going to bath houses and "hooking up with men participating in gay orgies." One of his patient's parents anonymously reported him to his work and the practice did a routine search of his computer, finding all sorts of downloads of gay men, adolescents and boys. He was immediately arrested for child pornography and lost his medical license. His family was devastated and yet his wife stayed with him throughout his trial and his incarceration in prison. Now he is home, and he is following all of his recovery tools and he has four years of clean time. But as one can imagine, his relationship had been severely traumatized.

The following is an excerpt from one of our sessions with Tom using AVR to increase empathy and fortify the coupleship.

Sandra: "I can't stand how I feel. It is like my whole body is affected. I don't want to go out. I wonder who is talking about me. I wonder if they think that I am crazy to still be with you. I hate my life, but I am scared to leave."

She looks at me and says, "I love Mark, but I don't know how to get over my anger at his addiction and his choices. I also wonder if he is staying with me because he can. How can he be attracted to me if he wanted to be with men? Or if he had an obsession with boys? I am really sick to my stomach."

I move them both into chairs that face each other. Mark starts by acknowledging Sandra's pain.

ACKNOWLEDGEMENT

- Mark: "I know it is so difficult to reckon with all the ways that I have hurt you. I want you to know that I can see your deep pain and confusion. It sounds like you feel stuck and you wonder if you will ever recover from the trauma that I have caused."

VALIDATION

- Mark: "I can feel the anger that you have for me and for yourself.

  And I heard you say that it is making you feel sick to your stomach."

REASSURANCE

- Mark: "I know it would be hard to have confidence in my efforts to be in good recovery, but I want you to know that you are the most important thing to me, and I will do whatever it takes to make you feel safe. I continue to remind myself of the pain that I have caused you, and I constantly ask myself, what does Sandra need to feel better? I love you and will do whatever I need to do to work through this. What do you need from me right now?"

Sandra told Mark that she was considering an informal separation so that she could spend some time by herself to determine what was really in her best interest.

NOTE: When you use AVR, there is no guarantee that things work out for the better, but since Mark is in true recovery, he told Sandra that he could stay with his mother to give her some breathing room.

SPOUSES ARE ABLE TO FORGIVE AND MOVE AHEAD, BUT THEY HAVE TO KNOW

THAT THE ADDICT IS GENUINELY SORRY AND IS WORKING ON HIS SOBRIETY

WITH A VENGEANCE.

Your spouse will need to be assured that you have put her first relationally and will work on your integrity and honesty. Integrity and honesty are at the core of relapse prevention!

HERE IS ANOTHER EXAMPLE OF AVR:

Tony and Marla were a couple who had been married for 37 years. She had caught him on several occasions looking at pornography and feared that he may have cheated outside of their marriage. One day during a normal gynecological exam, she was told by her doctor that there appeared to be an infection. After waiting several days, she found out that she had chlamydia and syphilis. She was horrified. She went to Tony and confronted him immediately. He broke down and shared with her that he could no longer carry on his dual life, and that he needed to come clean and admit to all of his wrongdoing. Tony confessed that he had cheated with hundreds of prostitutes. They spent from 3:00 p.m. to 4:00 a.m. talking about his addiction.

Marla was devastated. She was heartbroken that the man that she thought she knew had been this monster sleeping in her bed, sharing every possible and conceivable germ infestation with her.

How could he have betrayed her? How could he have exposed her to sexually transmitted illnesses? How could he have acted like a loving and caring father and husband and held the secret from her? It took many months of working together and working separately before any progress was made.

Tony admitted that he was willing to do the hard work to start a solid recovery program. He started attending ninety 12-step meetings in ninety days and he got a sponsor so that he could be guided in the right direction.

Marla put a filter system on all of his computers and his phone. She also began to track him with GPS. She went in for monthly checkups to make sure that she was physically in good health. She also asked him to go for monthly checkups as well.

As the couple started making progress, and Tony continued his good recovery, they had a full-fledged disclosure so that Marla would know everything. His disclosure was 32 pages long, and literally left all of us feeling exhausted.

In early recovery work, it is important for the addict to be in good recovery, and to have the accountability tools in place, so that the partner knows that she is safe. Therefore, it was imperative that after the disclosure, Tony receive a polygraph test. He then agreed to a polygraph test every four months for the next five years.

What both Marla and Tony were most concerned about was their communication. Tony would go into a deep spiral of shame, and Marla would doubt Tony's sincerity. This couple was in dire need of communication skills, reflective listening, mirroring, and AVR. Tony needed to continue to find ways to empathize with his wife without taking on the shame he felt. He constantly fought the belief that indeed his addiction had turned him into a monster.

Here are some excerpts from their therapy sessions as Tony learned AVR:

Marla came in and announced that this would be her last session. She was so disgusted with her husband that she could no longer tolerate his insensitivities to what he had done to her. She said that she would never trust him and that she would stay married, but she could not expect him to change because even if he did, she would never be able to trust him again...EVER.

Tony hung his head in shame, and I knew that Marla was likely taking a break from this painful situation.

Me: "Marla, I want to support you in any way that I can. I clearly hear that you are done for right now. You don't want to work on things because even if they appear to change, it is likely that you will not be able to trust the change because you have been so betrayed. You are tired of working so hard 'in vain.' Did I get that right?"

Marla: "That is exactly right. I am so tired and exhausted that my brain literally hurts! I ask myself, "Why should I trust him...he is probably lying to me again. I mean I don't think he would intentionally lie right now but I don't think he even knows when he is lying to himself. I just can't trust him, and I am not sure that I will ever be able to trust him again."

Me: "Well, since this is your last session, would you be willing to dialogue with Tony so that I can continue to help him learn the skills he needs to build a connection with you and the kids even if you decide to terminate your relationship with him emotionally or physically?"

Marla: "That would be fine."

Me: "Since I was chatting with Marla, I was wondering if you could use Focused Listening with her, so I make sure you heard her accurately. Once I am convinced that you heard what she was really saying than I will ask you to use AVR. Tony would you repeat back what you heard her say?"

Tony: "Marla, I heard you say that this would be your last session. You are so disgusted with me, you don't trust me, and basically, you hate me. You are going to stay married to me, but you will never trust me again, and you will never believe I have truly changed, no matter what I do."

(As you can see Tony interpreted what she said to mean that she hated him. He had plunged deep into his shame and heard what his own inner critic said, which was "I hate you, and I will never trust you again." In reality, she had said that she wasn't sure she would ever be able to trust him again.)

Marla clarified her thoughts with him and this time he repeated it accurately.

NOW IT WAS TIME TO DO AVR.

They sat knees-to-knees, looking directly into each other's eyes as he acknowledged her thoughts.

ACKNOWLEDGEMENT:

"Marla you have come to this session understandably tired. I have put you through so much agony and you are exhausted. As you look at the cost benefit of our relationship, you are doubtful that you will ever be able to trust me again because I have spent so much of our life deceiving you. This has caused you to not only mistrust me, but you also can't trust your own intuition."

Marla started to cry.

VALIDATION:

"You are incredibly sad that your whole life has been a lie, and I have shaken your sense of reality. You are not willing to keep putting out energy without proof that I am really changing. You are likely done."

Marla nodded and sat with a bowed head, tears streaming down her face.

REASSURANCE:

"I am sitting here wanting to reassure you, but recognizing that I need to respect your boundaries. You need to stop the therapy to honor your need to rest from this excruciating pain. The selfish me wants to tell you that I will get a second job to afford a monthly polygraph test to reassure you of my recovery, and I would do anything to make you feel safe right now. But I also want you to know that I clearly heard you say you need to withdraw from coming to therapy because it is a painful reminder of what was, what is, and what might not be. Did I get that right?"

Marla looked up at him and shook her head yes.

Tony reassured her, "I will do whatever it takes to make you feel safe. Whatever it takes!"

AVR looks easy, but in reality you have so much shame and guilt for the damage that you have caused that the process can be daunting and can feel unnatural at first. The addict typically wants to go into hiding and isolate when he experiences so much pain. It takes a lot of courage and skill to practice facing your fears head on and practicing this technique even when it looks like it is not working. You have to commit to the process of empathy just like you have committed to your process of recovery!

To practice this process, I want you to imagine being your wife and write out five frightening experiences that she might encounter in a normal day. Here are some excerpts from 3 previous clients who have used this process in their homework assignments.

1. I am frightened because you told me that a new woman has joined your staff and she is attractive and in her early 30's. I am afraid that you will be tempted to act out and then you will deceive me, and this process will start all over again. Even though you say you have told me everything about her and have answered all my questions, my mind is racing, my fears are overwhelming me, and it actually feels like it is happening right now!

2. I am sick to my stomach because they have opened another strip club called "Cheaters" right down the street, and I can't help but worry that you will be triggered and betray me again. I hate living in a society that openly promotes sex and I don't feel safe in my own neighborhood!

3. I am miserable because I don't feel like I will ever have a normal vacation again. We have to pick places where women will wear a lot of clothes while my favorite vacation is being on the beach, listening to the waves and feeling the sun on my face. You have contaminated my happy place and have changed vacations forever!

In the first scenario my client wrote out the following:

I am frightened because you told me that a new woman has joined your staff and she is attractive and in her early 30's. I am afraid that you will be tempted to act out and then you will deceive me, and this process will start all over again. Even though you say you have told me everything about her and have answered all my questions, my mind is racing, my fears are overwhelming me, and it actually feels like it is happening right now!

- **Acknowledgment** of the Issue: I can imagine that you are frightened because I told you that a new woman has joined our staff, and she is attractive and in her early 30's. And I can understand why you are afraid that I will be tempted to act out and will relapse into my sexually addictive behaviors and deceive you, and this process will start all over again.

- **Validation** of Feelings: I hear you saying that your mind is racing, and your fears are overwhelming you and you are basically terrified because it actually feels like it is happening right now.

- **Reassurance**: I want you to know that you have every right to feel this way based on my past. But I am working hard on my recovery and that the new employee doesn't affect me in the least. The only woman I want in my life is you, and I thank God every day that you have stuck by me through this process.

Here is another AVR a client wrote about his wife's feelings in the second scenario:

I am sick to my stomach because they have opened another strip club called "Cheaters" right down the street, and I can't help but worry that you will be triggered and betray me again. I hate living in a society that openly promotes sex and I just don't ever feel safe in my neighborhood!

- **Acknowledgment** of the Issue: I can see why you are sick to your stomach because they have opened another strip club called "Cheaters" right down the street. And I know that you are worried because you know how sick I was and how this addiction hijacked my brain, and so you fear that I will be triggered and betray you again.

- **Validation** of Feelings: I understand why you are worried and anxious about my sobriety. You feel overwhelmed with fear that I might get triggered by this club.

- **Reassurance**: I get why you would hate living in a society that openly promotes sex because I have those same feelings now that I am in good recovery. I want both of us to feel safe in our neighborhood. I want you to know that being in good recovery has totally shaped my view on how sick our society can be and how sick I was when I was in active addiction. My 12 Step program has helped me to see what is important in my life and that is my integrity and my family and you. I am never going back to my old ways again.

In the 3rd scenario my client wrote out the following response in his homework assignment:

I am miserable because I don't feel like I will ever have a normal vacation again. We have to pick places where women will wear a lot of clothes while my favorite vacation is being on the beach, listening to the waves, and feeling the sun on my face. You have contaminated my happy place and have changed vacations forever!

- **Acknowledgment** of the Issue: I hear that you are miserable because you don't feel like you will ever have a normal vacation again. You have to pick places where women will wear a lot of clothes and you can never relax and pick a place where you want to go. Your favorite vacation is being on the beach, listening to the waves and feeling the sun on your face, and I have contaminated your happy place and have changed vacations forever.

- **Validation** of Feelings: I can understand why you would be angry and resentful that I have robbed you of your favorite vacations.

- **Reassurance**: I can only say that one day I hope that my recovery is strong enough to go anywhere in the world that we want without fear. I know it would not be a wise thing to do right now, but I am working towards liberation from all my sexual compulsions, and the Green Book promises that if I work the program, I will one day be free from compulsive thoughts!

USING AVR WITH HER FEARS

So now that you have some examples of what other recovering addicts have written, it is your turn to think back to some frequent fears that your wife has experienced. Through the use of the Empathy formula AVR, write 3-5 examples and her concerns.

FEAR / CONCERN # 1:

Acknowledge Her Fear / Concern / Issue:

Validate Her Feelings:

Reassure Her:

FEAR / CONCERN # 2:

Acknowledge Her Fear / Concern / Issue:

Validate Her Feelings:

Reassure Her:

FEAR / CONCERN # 3:

Acknowledge Her Fear / Concern / Issue:

Validate Her Feelings:

Reassure Her:

FEAR / CONCERN # 4:

Acknowledge Her Fear / Concern / Issue:

Validate Her Feelings:

Reassure Her:

FEAR / CONCERN # 5:
Acknowledge Her Fear / Concern / Issue:
Validate Her Feelings:
Reassure Her:

I know that writing these fears and concerns out can feel laborious, but this is a very important process and one that will REALLY make a difference in your relationship. Therefore, you want to get it right and do it well.

Remember that you spent a lot of time lying to her, deceiving her, and gaslighting her, and so now, your communication needs to be heartfelt, honest and authentic.

My experience with working with the male population is that you did not learn empathy skills in your childhood. This may be the first time you have concentrated on learning it and using it, so it will take some work. There is a saying the 12-Step Community uses that "when you work it...it works!" That saying applies here, so don't short change the process!

WHEN YOU WORK AVR, IT WORKS!

Sexual betrayal affects both you and your wife and therefore your recovery means finding healthy supports and tools to practice sexual sobriety and healthy relational skills and techniques to rebuild and restore your relationship!

The APSATS model teaches clinicians and coaches that you have to participate in good recovery to establish the foundation for your wife's safety and stabilization.

You then need to be there for her and help her through the intense grief that she is experiencing. This includes walking with her through all the stages of grief like anger, sadness and depression. AVR will assist you both in communicating about what she is experiencing as a result of your sexual addiction. This phase of partner betrayal recovery work can take anywhere from 1-3 years as she toggles back and forth from safety to grief.

SHE MAY ALWAYS EXPERIENCE TRIGGERS, BUT SHE WILL BE BETTER ABLE TO MANAGE THEM IF YOU CAN HELP HER HEAL.

The natural evolution of her recovery will occur when she comes to an acceptance of what has happened to her, combined with seeing your good recovery and active involvement with making her feel safe. Then, you can both focus on restoring the relationship.

RESTORING THE RELATIONSHIP

This last step in your relational recovery is that you not only have established better communication and empathy, but you are participating in healthy behaviors as a couple to strengthen your relationship as a team. This might look like going to church or synagogue together, attending small groups or bible studies, taking vacations together as a couple, writing love letters to each other, attending healthy seminars like the 5 Love Languages, attending marital retreats, and practicing the daily skills like shutting phones off at 7 PM, or taking walks, or reading scripture together.

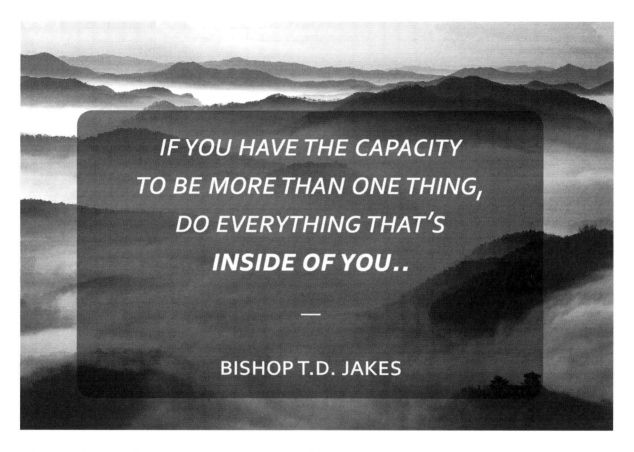

IF YOU HAVE THE CAPACITY TO BE MORE THAN ONE THING, DO EVERYTHING THAT'S INSIDE OF YOU..

—

BISHOP T.D. JAKES

In working a healthy program, an addict must work on his "3 Circles" and add to his 3rd circle which is creating healthy habits for his recovery. In working as a couple, it is important to build healthy habits that will build on the love you have for each other.

SEXUAL BETRAYAL AFFECTS BOTH YOU AND YOUR WIFE. THEREFORE, YOUR RECOVERY MEANS FINDING HEALTHY SUPPORTS AND TOOLS TO PRACTICE SEXUAL SOBRIETY AND RELATIONAL HEALTHY SKILLS AND TECHNIQUES TO REBUILD AND RESTORE YOUR RELATIONSHIP!

HEALTHY BEHAVIORS AND PRACTICES

What are the healthy behaviors that you and your spouse have incorporated into your life now that you have been working on your relational skills and your recovery is strong and stabilized?

List 10 new activities that the two of you are doing together.

1. _____

2. _____

3. _____

4. _____

5. _____

6. _____

7. _____

8. _____

_____

9. _____

_____

10. _____

_____

What are 5 other activities that you would like to add to your repertoire of healthy behaviors?

1. _____

_____

2. _____

_____

3. _____

_____

4. _____

_____

5. _____

_____

CHAPTER 6
COMMUNICATION

COMMUNICATION

There are many types of communication, and in high conflict and stressful situations, a couple will resort to one of four types of communication to respond to that stress. As you know, your partner has been traumatized and may vacillate from being so angry that she responds aggressively to checking out and giving you the silent treatment (passive or passive aggressive.) Her defense mechanisms have caused her to protect herself and stay safe from possible on-going unfaithfulness, gaslighting, and betrayals. You will need to model healthy communication and listening skills by validating her feelings and fears.

After working with thousands of addicts, I know that you have work to do on improving your communication too. It is not uncommon for you to get discouraged when she doesn't trust your new recovery, and you will want to lash out to her too (aggressive style). And at times, you will want to say, "Oh forget it" and walk away (passive or passive-aggressive) which does not resolve the situation.

There are four types of communication. Look at each type and see if you can come up with ways that you have responded to her in each category.

YOU WANT TO STRIVE FOR GENTLE ASSERTIVENESS

Assertiveness is being clear and direct about what you need and want. It does not mean you will get what you want; it means you have stated your feelings and facts clearly. When you assert yourself, your loved ones or coworkers will know where you stand. It does not mean that you get your way, but it does send a clear message of how you feel, what you believe, and what you may need. It is the first step to creating other forms of healthy behaviors, like increasing your communication or setting up boundaries that would keep you both safe or developing consequences with others if they violate your boundaries. It enables you to set limits so that others won't walk all over you. It creates healthy boundaries and enables you to accomplish goals because it reinforces what's important to you.

Your partner may also have had trouble expressing assertiveness and sharing her feelings and thoughts. Although women are inherently better communicators, they may have kept some of their feelings to themselves to avoid conflict or to promote harmony.

Many of my partners have spent so much time attending to the needs of others that they rob themselves of the satisfaction of achieving their own goals. If self-esteem is solely based on doing for others, the person will not have the opportunity to know what he or she wants. Learning assertiveness will bring clarity to one's own needs.

 # YOUR ASSERTIVENESS HISTORY

Think of 3 times that you were clear and direct about how you felt or what you wanted.

1.

2.

3.

PASSIVENESS

Are you or your spouse passive? People who are passive are easily overlooked or walked on. This allows others to control them or not to understand what is going on in their lives. If you are passive, you probably present with poor self-esteem. Deep down, you feel that your opinion does not count. Perhaps there is so much shame wrapped up in what you have done, and you don't feel you deserve to stand up for what you feel or believe. John Gottman calls this "stonewalling," and says when you walk away from conflict, then nothing can get resolved, and that you are contributing to further problems in the relationship. It can be helpful to take time out to assess your feelings or gather your thoughts, but not to walk out permanently from the conflict or communication.

 EXERCISE List 3 ways in your past that you exhibited passive communication & let things happen because it was easier or safer than working it out.

1.
2.
3.

AGGRESSIVENESS

As an addict, you may have found that you protected your addiction by lashing out aggressively with your family. People who communicate aggressively are trying to communicate by intimidation. You may have bullied your spouse and seemed very threatening to her to shut her down and to protect your addiction.

The aggressive personality type attacks the character of others and appears very demanding. They can make you feel put down. People who communicate aggressively typically want to control and dominate others. They may try to intimidate a person into doing it "their way." Many addicts have confessed that they communicated aggressively to stop their spouse from figuring out about the addiction. When the addict uses aggressiveness, there is an element of gaslighting that occurs. The spouse who is trying to figure out what is really going on ends up feeling crazy because the addict is attacking her for her vigilance. It ends up being a double betrayal.

 Have you been aggressive in your communication and behavior with others? List 3 ways you have related to your wife aggressively.

1.
2.
3.

PASSIVE-AGGRESSIVE

Many partners complained that when their spouse was in full addiction he appeared to be very passive-aggressive. Addicts would leave for work and not come home on time. They would not answer their phone for hours. They would use DARVO techniques on the partner.

DARVO is a type of communication that addicts might use when they were being held accountable for their behavior. It was coined by Jennifer Freyd and stands for *deny, attack, reverse victim* and *offender*. When an addict didn't come home after work because he was acting out, he might deny his actions and attack the partner for confronting him, telling her that she was controlling and reversing the scenario to make her feel that she was constantly discouraging, blaming and angry. He would accuse her of sending him messages that he couldn't do anything right. He would appear to be the victim and she the offender.

Addicts who are passive-aggressive are angry and will get even with people behind their backs. People who forget appointments that they don't want to attend or who do not answer a question because they don't want to talk about things may be relating in a passive-aggressive manner. Addicts may disappear, do what they want, then deny their behavior. Often, addicts conduct themselves in this fashion to protect their addiction.

 Can you think of times that you used DARVO or passive-aggressive behaviors to hide your acting out?

1.
2.
3.

MEN WHO ARE IN EARLY RECOVERY MAY NOT BE ABLE TO IDENTIFY THE UNHEALTHY FORMS OF BEHAVIOR. HOWEVER, AFTER THEY HAVE WORKED ON THEIR RELATIONAL SKILLS, THEY ARE ABLE TO REVIEW THEIR PAST AND QUICKLY OWN THEIR OLD UNHEALTHY FORMS OF MANIPULATION.

As you can see, out of the four types of behaviors, assertiveness is the goal. Since the discovery, it may seem difficult to use assertiveness because you feel you have no right to share your true feelings and thoughts. But a relationship cannot heal unless there is honesty between both people.

YOU MAY NEED TO JOURNAL TO ENCOURAGE YOURSELF TO DECIDE WHAT IS THE BEST WAY TO HONESTLY SHARE YOUR THOUGHTS.

It is important to be gentle because she is highly dysregulated and will not know if she can trust your honesty and assertiveness.

I typically teach couples to practice the following formula to use assertiveness because it includes an explanation of your own personal perceptions of what you believe is going on.

ASSERTIVENESS: THE KEY TO GOOD SELF-ESTEEM

As I indicated, assertiveness does not mean you will always get what you want... but you know that you were clear about what you thought, felt and needed. It helps you own your own perceptions. It may create some conflict, but know that if you are being honest, you must face the conflict so that she can know where you stand and know your feelings and truth. It will be important to use a gentle tone as you share your thoughts and feelings to decrease the possibility of triggering her.

As you share your thoughts, it will likely take her to a place where she initially reminds you that you betrayed her and did not allow her to have a voice. This is true. Your addiction robbed her of a safe place to have an honest, authentic connection, so make sure to validate her experience before you proceed to assertiveness.

The formula below will help you to identify situations that you would like to change. It is very easy to use and begins with addressing your concerns by using her name.

- *Sandy, when you get frustrated with me for being late, I feel sad because the message it sends me is that you are sure that I am acting out again.*

- *Faith, when you go through my texts and demand to know who this person is, I feel irritated because the message it sends me is that you still think I am keeping things from you.*

- *Sarah, when you talk about our problems in front of the kids, I feel scared because the message it sends me is that I will never be able to redeem myself in their eyes.*

The reality of your assertiveness statement is that she will confirm that she does fear that you are acting out or she is afraid that you are keeping things from her. You may want to alter the sentence with:

What I fear most is: _____

_____

- *Sandy, when you get frustrated with me for being late, I feel sad because what I fear most is that you will never believe that I am in good recovery and not acting out anymore.*

- *Faith, when you go through my texts and demand to know who this person is, I fear that you will not believe that I truly don't know, and you will understandably go to the fear that I am acting out.*

- *Sarah, when you talk about our problems in front of the kids, I feel scared because what I fear most is that the kids will be confused and not be able to process our adult conversation.*

THE ASSERTIVENESS FORMULA:

_____, when you _____
(Name)   (Name the specific behavior)

I feel or felt _____
                          (Pick a specific feeling)

because _____
                          (The message it sent me was)

OR

_____, when you _____
(Name)   (Name the specific behavior)

I feel or felt _____
                          (Pick a specific feeling)

because what I fear most is _____

_____

CHAPTER 7
CONFLICT

CONFLICT IN A HEALTHY RELATIONSHIP BREEDS INTIMACY.

CAROL JUERGENSEN SHEETS

CONFLICT

It is normal to have conflict in your relationship and when you work through it, it can actually bring about a greater closeness. However, after betrayal trauma, your work around conflict will need to go into overdrive. When your spouse learns about sexual addiction, the conflict is heightened, and it is your job to find safe ways of bringing it back to a more normal and regulated state. I have developed the following formula to keep you in your window of tolerance as you help the relationship weather the casualty of the inherent conflict that accompanies partner and sexual betrayal.

CONFLICT AFTER BETRAYAL

THE 7 PRINCIPLES OF DEALING WITH CONFLICT AFTER BETRAYAL©:

There is so much crisis management in early recovery work. The partner is devastated and is experiencing so much conflict with the addict and within herself. The feelings of anger and conflict can feel insurmountable. Addicts need to find ways of navigating through the conflict, holding themselves accountable and yet not going down the shame spiral.

I want to teach you a technique that will help you stay in good recovery and will help you stay out of the shame cycle as you help her to heal.

1. When you experience conflict, ask yourself: How has my past contributed to the present-day conflict? Recognize the other 90% is about your past and not who you are today.

2. Hold yourself accountable for causing the pain while not going into shame mode.

3. Know that although her pain is a direct response to your past actions, it is not in response to who you are today.

4. Recognize that you are strong enough to be a container for her pain. You can help her work through her own trauma and move beyond it, while you work on your own solid recovery.

5. Tell yourself the issue is not about you, but about a trauma response from your acting out in the past.

6. Practice saying... "This is not who I am today. This is about the consequences of my past actions." Know that your addiction is your kryptonite, and your recovery is your antidote.

7. Tell yourself: "I won't give my past guilt and shame the power to make me feel _____

   (Sad, Shameful, Inadequate, Unworthy, Angry...)

When you apply this formula, it helps you to keep your feelings in perspective which will give you strength to help her heal!

Make a copy of this list and keep it visible so that you can practice these 7 principles.

(EXERCISE) APPLYING THE 7 PRINCIPLES OF CONFLICT AFTER BETRAYAL

Now think of a time where your spouse revisited how devastated she has felt. Write out the issue, and then apply the 7 principles to getting past the conflict.

Her Issue/Fear About You: _____

_____

_____

_____

_____

_____

_____

APPLY THE 7 PRINCIPLES OF CONFLICT AFTER BETRAYAL:

1. How has your past contributed to your present-day problems? Remember 90% is about your past and not who you are today.

_____

_____

_____

_____

_____

2. How can you hold yourself accountable for the pain you caused without going into the shame cycle?

_____

_____

_____

_____

_____

3. Remind yourself that although your past caused the pain, it is not in response to who you are today.

_____

_____

_____

_____

_____

4. How will you recognize that you are strong enough to be a container for her pain? How can you help her work through her own trauma and move beyond it, while you work on your own solid recovery?

_____

_____

_____

_____

_____

5. How do you remind yourself that the issue is not about you, but about a trauma response from your acting out in the past?

_____

_____

_____

_____

6. Practice saying, "This is not who I am today. This is about the consequences of my past actions." How am I recognizing that these are the consequences of my past actions while simultaneously realizing that I can only stay healthy if I practice good recovery?

_____

_____

_____

_____

7. How can I tell myself: "I won't give my past guilt and shame the power to make me feel _____? How do you feel and what word would best describe your feelings?

_____

_____

_____

_____

CHAPTER 8
TECHNIQUES THAT KEEP YOU STRONG
WHILE YOU HELP HER HEAL

TECHNIQUES THAT KEEP YOU STRONG WHILE YOU HELP HER HEAL

TECHNIQUES TO KEEP YOU STRONG WHEN SHE REJECTS YOUR ATTEMPTS TO HELP HER HEAL BECAUSE SHE IS TRAUMATIZED

There is no doubt that the couples we work with are hungering for emotional intimacy. Both the addict and the partner are wanting to establish closeness, and yet typically the partner is afraid to trust that it is real, so she puts up her guard and will subtly reject the addict's attempts at honesty, authenticity, and transparency. The addict's self-esteem has been crushed from his addiction. He is especially vulnerable to criticism and rejection. He has to muster all his strength to weather the constant underpinnings of the partner pushing him away.

It has been said that the greatest gift that you can give your wife in her recovery is for her to be completely honest with her feelings and for her to be able to share her anger. Remember I said that in "healthy" relationships, "conflict breeds intimacy."

After a fracture has occurred, there is nothing healthy about your relationship. One of the goals is to restore the relationship and to create a place where you can experience conflict and work through it so that she feels heard, validated and understood. This requires that you hear it, feel the appropriate accompanying feelings, and yet stay out of the shame cycle. Instead, you can ask yourself, what can I do to keep from going into shame and isolation? There is a process that I teach called "Spraying Yourself with Teflon."

THE TEFLON TECHNIQUE©

I often teach young kids that when they are being criticized or bullied, they can spray themselves with Teflon, to let the personal attacks roll right off without going into low self-esteem.

While addicts need to hear the sadness, anger and pain in their spouses' words, they need to be able to refrain from internalizing it to avoid the shame cycle. They also need to avoid the tendency to defend, rationalize or minimize what they have done. They need to be "the container" and hold the feelings their spouse is having so that she can explain, vent, describe, and express them to externalize them as part of her healing process. When you are able to hold or contain those feelings, she will grieve and process her feelings, and she will be more likely to move on in her processing of the betrayal.

Addicts typically want to know "How long will this process take?" Their fear is that it will last a lifetime. Many of the addicts that I work with in group therapy answer the question by saying, "You know, we have been gaslighting our partners for years and years, and so this process will likely require lots of patience and time to get through the pain."

Using the Teflon Technique assists you in hearing her without giving up on the relationship. When I explain to the betrayed partner the process of Teflon, she usually fears that her husband won't feel her pain. This is a very understandable concern due to the lack of empathy in the old relationship. But I remind her that he is developing empathy. It is imperative that he be able to moderate his internalization of her pain to stay out of the shame cycle and to keep his defense mechanisms from taking over. I also remind her that in all her pain and suffering her tendency may be to "fight" her way through it, and I want him to protect himself in case her brain gets hijacked because of her pain. I remind her that the partner sensitive model from which I work maintains that if the partner decides to stay with the addict, the addict will need to learn the skills to help her heal and create a "living amends." This requires that he fortify the relationship which will make her feel safe and will help boost his self-esteem!

> THE ADDICT WILL NEED TO LEARN THE SKILLS TO HELP HER HEAL AND CREATE A "LIVING AMENDS" WHICH REQUIRES THAT HE FORTIFY THE RELATIONSHIP WHICH WILL MAKE HER FEEL SAFE AND WILL HELP BOOST HIS SELF-ESTEEM!

It is important for you to acknowledge the ways that you are supporting your wife in her healing. We ask couples to identify the small changes they are making in their relationship and to share that during check-ins with each other. We also ask addicts to start a gratitude journal which includes things that have improved since discovery. We want you to know that there are great strides that both of you are making and that it is important to note them to measure the changes and successes in your relationship.

 ## YOUR RECOVERY GRATITUDE JOURNAL

Each day, for at least 10 minutes, note some successes from the previous day. An entry might look like:

- I helped my wife through a trigger when the anniversary date of discovery occurred yesterday. I left her a letter sharing why I am so grateful that she stayed with me.

- My wife actually let me put my arm around her without pulling away.

- I have a good daily practice of doing my recovery reading which strengthens my recovery and shows my partner that I am working hard on my recovery.

- I told my wife to put her feet up while I put our 3 kids to bed.

- I called my wife when I left from work 3 minutes late and offered to pick up Starbucks on the way home.

What might your first 3 entries be from yesterday?

1. _____
   _____
   _____
   _____
   _____
   _____

2. _____
   _____
   _____
   _____
   _____
   _____

3. _____
   _____
   _____
   _____
   _____

CHAPTER 9

WAYS TO DEVELOP

INTIMACY

EMPATHY AND INTIMACY

When empathy has been firmly established and practiced, intimacy will naturally grow. Take a look at these behaviors and decide how well you and your partner are doing with achieving the safety to work through the feelings, issues, and behavioral changes that occur when healing from sexual betrayal.

HOW DO YOU INCREASE EMOTIONAL INTIMACY?

Laura Dawn Lewis coined the concept of the *Eight Stages of Intimacy* (The Couples Company, 2004). One of the eight stages is emotional intimacy which covers feelings, trust, security and safety in a relationship. Many couples never achieve emotional intimacy because you have to accept your partner for who he or she is without reservation. At this level of intimacy, the couple feels comfortable sharing anger, happiness, secrets, sensual and sexual feelings. Each of you know you are loved and love your partner, no matter how either of you feel or act.

In sexual and porn addiction, there is so much wounding that the emotional intimacy is diminished, and it becomes difficult for the wounded partner to feel comfortable enough to share anger, happiness and erotic feelings. Some spouses call for a sexual cooling off period of celibacy, so the addict can heal the addiction's damage to the brain and don't feel safe enough to engage in sexual activity until they can trust their partner once again.

 ## THE EMOTIONAL INTIMACY CONTINUUM

To build intimacy and empathy, the wounded partner needs to know that the addict understands the pain is due to the addict's poor choices and not the wounded partner's fault. Emotional intimacy is achieved when trust is established again, and the couple can speak about sensitive topics without constantly bringing up past indiscretions.

Here are some examples of how to build intimacy with empathy. Rate each area from 1 to 10 where 1 represents that you are not currently able to achieve the goal and 10 represents that you have mastered it.

1a. In a state of fear, uncertainty, or danger, your partner is the person you turn to for comfort.

1	2	3	4	5	6	7	8	9	10

NOT GOOD   WORKING ON IT   CLOSE TO MASTERY

1b. In a state of fear, uncertainty, or danger, you are the person your partner turns to for comfort.

1	2	3	4	5	6	7	8	9	10

NOT GOOD   WORKING ON IT   CLOSE TO MASTERY

2a. You cry, show frustration, sadness or anger in front of your partner, and you know this is healthy. You know she will not see you as weak, psychotic, crazy, or out of control.

1	2	3	4	5	6	7	8	9	10

NOT GOOD   WORKING ON IT   CLOSE TO MASTERY

2b. Your partner can cry, show frustration, sadness or anger in front of you, and know that she is safe. You will not see her as weak, psychotic, crazy or out of control.

1	2	3	4	5	6	7	8	9	10

NOT GOOD   WORKING ON IT   CLOSE TO MASTERY

3a. You can speak about sex, secrets, and your feelings without a fear of being betrayed, ridiculed, or compromised.

1	2	3	4	5	6	7	8	9	10

NOT GOOD   WORKING ON IT   CLOSE TO MASTERY

3b. She can speak about sex, secrets, and her feelings without a fear of being betrayed, ridiculed, or compromised.

1	2	3	4	5	6	7	8	9	10

NOT GOOD   WORKING ON IT   CLOSE TO MASTERY

4a. No matter what happens, you know your partner loves you and will not abandon you during your recovery.

1	2	3	4	5	6	7	8	9	10

NOT GOOD   WORKING ON IT   CLOSE TO MASTERY

4b. No matter what happens, you love your partner and will not abandon her while she processes the betrayal recovery.

1	2	3	4	5	6	7	8	9	10

NOT GOOD   WORKING ON IT   CLOSE TO MASTERY

5a. You show or tell your partner often, through words and actions, that you love and respect her.

1	2	3	4	5	6	7	8	9	10

NOT GOOD   WORKING ON IT   CLOSE TO MASTERY

5b. She shows or tells you often, through words and actions, that she is seeing your progress and respects the recovery that you are doing.

1	2	3	4	5	6	7	8	9	10

NOT GOOD   WORKING ON IT   CLOSE TO MASTERY

6a. You are becoming less defensive when she brings up past wrongs.

1	2	3	4	5	6	7	8	9	10

NOT GOOD   WORKING ON IT   CLOSE TO MASTERY

6b. You realize that her anger or defensiveness is her way to protect herself.

1	2	3	4	5	6	7	8	9	10

NOT GOOD   WORKING ON IT   CLOSE TO MASTERY

6c. The relationship is healing, and the past is discussed, forgiven, and left there.

1	2	3	4	5	6	7	8	9	10

NOT GOOD   WORKING ON IT   CLOSE TO MASTERY

NOTE: *This may take some time recovering from sexual betrayal, but when both partners work on healing themselves, the chances of recapturing the intimacy can be achieved through empathy for each other.*

6d. She is not bringing up past wrongs as frequently.

1	2	3	4	5	6	7	8	9	10

NOT GOOD   WORKING ON IT   CLOSE TO MASTERY

6e. They are not being dredged up in arguments as much, indicating that she is healing.

1	2	3	4	5	6	7	8	9	10

NOT GOOD   WORKING ON IT   CLOSE TO MASTERY

6f. The past is discussed, forgiven and left there most of the time.

1	2	3	4	5	6	7	8	9	10
NOT GOOD				WORKING ON IT				CLOSE TO MASTERY	

7a. You deal with conflict fairly and do not resort to passive-aggressive, aggressive or stalemating behavior when there is conflict in your relationship.

1	2	3	4	5	6	7	8	9	10
NOT GOOD				WORKING ON IT				CLOSE TO MASTERY	

7b. She does not resort to passive-aggressive, aggressive or stalemating behavior when there is conflict in your relationship.

1	2	3	4	5	6	7	8	9	10
NOT GOOD				WORKING ON IT				CLOSE TO MASTERY	

This assessment tool is a great way to check in and decide what you want to work on and to be able to determine the progress you have made and are making in the relationship. You can jointly identify areas you want to work on and discuss them with your partner.

QUESTIONS TO DETERMINE EMOTIONAL INTIMACY

1. TO THE BETRAYED PARTNER: What will it take for you to feel safe in this relationship?

    _____

    _____

    _____

    _____

    _____

    TO THE ADDICT: What will it take for you to want to build trust within this relationship?

    _____

    _____

    _____

    _____

    _____

2. Can you show empathy when your parner has trouble trusting you?

    _____

    _____

    _____

    _____

    _____

3. Have you ever cried in front of your partner? Yes / No

4. If not, what is your fear about being this vulnerable?

    _____

    _____

    _____

    _____

    _____

5. What's the worst that can happen?

    _____

    _____

    _____

    _____

    _____

6. Has that ever happened? Yes / No

7. If yes, did your partner react with empathy or with scorn?

    Circle one: Empathy / Scorn

8. Why?

    _____

    _____

    _____

    _____

    _____

INTELLECT AND EMPATHY (CONNECTING YOUR HOPES, FEARS, OPINIONS AND BELIEFS)

Your character and motivation as an individual and couple says a lot about how empathetic you can be with your spouse. Sharing hopes, fears, opinions and beliefs builds a deep sense of trust within the relationship, revealing a deeper sense of self. When you have intellectual intimacy, you learn how to mirror each other, validate each other's point of view and engage in the exchange of ideas. All of these are empathic actions.

Other ways to show empathy intellectually include discussing fears and helping each other stay away from triggers and slippery slopes, especially when it comes to all forms of sexual addiction. Empathy means being able to state an opinion, which your spouse may not agree with, without fear of ridicule or embarrassment; and learning to accept "no" from your spouse without holding onto resentment or anger. We know this takes a while for the partner because she has been so betrayed by you. And yet you should see a gradual change in her ability to accept that you have changed and that you are a better person because of your recovery.

After recovery has been established and you are working on your empathy skills, you will likely question whether you have the right to hold on to your non-negotiable boundaries to protect or assert yourself. These include values and principles you hold dear and feel strongly about; such as religion, politics, types of sex, children, and education. Empathy would be like saying, "I understand how you feel about this, but this is a non-negotiable boundary for me at this time." It is important to understand these things about yourself so that you can share them with your spouse. Spend some time answering these questions and then reflect on them during your next check in or while you are on your next walk. Notice how your partner reacts to you and what her feedback is as you develop more intellectual intimacy in your relationship.

QUESTIONS TO DETERMINE INTELLECTUAL INTIMACY

- What is the biggest misconception people have about you?

  _____

  _____

  _____

  _____

  _____

- Where do you see yourself in the next five years? (Personal, family, job, coupleship, recovery)

  _____

  _____

  _____

  _____

  _____

- What do you consider to be your greatest accomplishment since your recovery?

  _____

  _____

  _____

  _____

  _____

- How do you define success?

  _____

  _____

_____

_____

_____

- What do you stand for and why?

_____

_____

_____

_____

_____

- Where do you stand on society's view of betrayal and do you think societal norms and values (or lack of them) play a part in the escalation of betrayal?

_____

_____

_____

_____

_____

Pay attention to the answers to these questions. Write down your answers and compare them with those of your partner. Serious relationship problems begin with a lack of empathy in intellectual intimacy. Societal norms, values and beliefs change rapidly, and our environment influences our actions and behaviors. For a partnership to succeed there must be congruent beliefs of right vs. wrong and empathy toward differences.

SEXUAL INTIMACY AND EMPATHY

In most cases, sexual intimacy is something that you learn as you navigate through life with your partner. People are uncomfortable about talking about sex, and therefore, sexual intimacy is learned based on trial and error. There is no doubt that when sexual addiction and partner betrayal occurs, that intimacy is fractured, sometimes never to be able to be rebuilt again.

If you are an addict who is in good recovery and are seeking to develop a closer relationship with your partner, it can feel intrusive to want to work on your sexual intimacy because of the damage that you have caused. You are showing good empathy because sex is likely not a safe topic and your wife is reeling from your sexual betrayal. Her sexuality has been extremely compromised. It is very important to check in with her about what she might need to feel physical closeness and to be extremely sensitive about her feelings, fears or anxiety about how she would like to proceed in the bedroom.

Sexual intimacy requires that you look for ways to be close and to develop trust in many different areas. It will be very necessary for you to check on the temperature of your wife's comfort level sexually. This means that you will need to check in with her frequently to find out how she is doing, what she is thinking, and what she needs to feel safe.

Just bringing up the topic may make your wife feel pressured. A partner sensitive therapist can help you both create a safe place to talk about the sexual wounding that has occurred. Go to APSATS.org to find a partner sensitive therapist or coach to help you in this area.

Regardless of whether your wife wants more sex, less sex, or no sex, you can look for ways to build on the closeness you will need to rebuild your sexual relationship.

When you nurture your wife in and outside of the bedroom, you're more likely to build on the trust, dependability, and empathy in your sexual relationship. Most couples have heard the old adage that "foreplay begins outside of the bedroom," and it is true that when you show her that you want to improve in all areas of her life, you will be building on the foundation that you need to rebuild trust and connection. Look for ways to care for the kids, do your fair share of household chores and duties, and seek closeness without sexuality. Since this relationship has been so damaged, it can be especially helpful to find ways of providing what Dr. Gary Chapman calls "in the Love Language - Acts of Service."

In *The Five Love Languages*, Dr. Chapman identifies physical touch, acts of service, quality time, words of affirmation, and gifts as being ways that you can show your love and build up that emotional love tank again. The most important thing is to freely do things for your wife without expecting sex in return. This builds a sense of safety and trust. When you attend to your partner's needs without expecting sex in return, she will know that every time you touch her, it does not mean you are manipulating her to gain sex. Otherwise it will become a manipulative relationship where she is confused about your intentions.

Empathy means understanding that you created this unsafe sexual environment and accepting your partner's physical or emotional dilemma. You recognize that this inhibits sex currently, and you understand her feelings. You are willing to pace her instead of coercing your partner into having sex anyway. It's a respect for her feelings, letting go of your own wants and needs for the good of the relationship.

Sex can be a difficult subject to talk about in any relationship, so it is important to examine some of your feelings about your current sexual relationship.

I have never in my work with sexual addiction met a sex addict who was comfortable talking about the sexual betrayal and the current state of the relationship's sexuality. This is a process and you DEFINITELY can develop more emotional IQ in this area.

So, find a quiet space and reflect on the following questions. Make sure to be honest with yourself when you answer them.

1. The reason that I am uncomfortable talking with my partner about my current sexual needs is:

_____

_____

_____

_____

_____

_____

2. My sexual betrayal has caused my wife to question her:

_____

_____

_____

_____

_____

3. When my partner is triggered or feels unsafe sexually I can show empathy by...

_____

_____

_____

_____

_____

4. List 5 ways you would like to be intimate with your partner, excluding sexual intercourse.

    » _____

    » _____

    » _____

    » _____

    » _____

5. List 5 things you can do around the house without being asked that will build the trust back into your relationship.

» _____

» _____

» _____

» _____

» _____

6. List 5 types of gifts, flowers, cards, etc. that you can sporadically give your partner when they least expect it.

» _____

» _____

» _____

» _____

» _____

The important thing in developing sexual empathy is to not get discouraged when your wife sets boundaries around her needs sexually. Your indiscretion has infiltrated every area of her life, but it can show up most as a sexual betrayal, so it makes sense that you pay close attention to what she needs or wants for sexual safety. It is your job to rebuild that sexual intimacy, but you will need to let her determine what she needs from you to make that happen. This involves a lot of communication and sometimes the best time to do that is in your daily or nightly check ins.

NOTE: In early recovery, you may need to request an abstinence contract for your own recovery safety. This allows your arousal template to calm down and increases good sobriety. Letting your wife know that you would like to abstain from sex may be triggering. Since this affects what she may need, you will have to explain all the reasons that it is good for your recovery. Make sure to explain the brain science around this abstinence because this can be very threatening to your wife, and you will need her support as it affects both of you.

CHAPTER 10

PROCESSES THAT MUST OCCUR BEFORE

EARLY RECOVERY COUPLE'S WORK

TRUST BUILDING PROCESS FOR THE COUPLESHIP

THE FORMAL DISCLOSURE

There is no way to right the wrong that has occurred when sexual addiction robs the addict of integrity and trust. The spouse and the family have been deeply affected. If trust is ever to be restored, it will require that the spouse learns the truth so that she can make an informed decision about what she wants or needs to proceed. We recommend that she participate in a formal disclosure.

In a formal disclosure, a therapist works closely with the addict to create a timeline of all his indiscretions from the time of meeting his spouse until present. The spouse may want to understand the history of how your addiction began so ask her where she wants you to start in this disclosure. Although this process is gut wrenching and raw, it helps the addict to reveal all of his secrets, and it allows the partner to hear the truth. This process usually takes 3-6 weeks for the addict to write out his timeline. His spouse is asked to list all of her questions that have to do with the "facts" of his acting out.

Sometimes a partner will have 20 questions that she wants the addict to answer in his disclosure and timeline. (I recently had a spouse who had 119 questions that she needed answered. She determines the number of her questions). He is to answer all questions that are fact based in the disclosure in conjunction with his acting out.

The disclosure can affect partners in many ways, but in general, most partners reported that they felt the disclosure was helpful in "stopping the bleeding." They were tired of the staggered disclosures and wanted a safe way to hear it all.

They were now able to see the addiction for what it was, and they felt devastated and yet relieved that they knew the truth.

After the disclosure, his wife accompanies him to the polygraph test to assure that he did reveal EVERYTHING that he could about his acting out. Sometimes, couples have to travel hundreds of miles to seek out a good polygrapher who understands sex addiction and is sensitive to partner betrayal.

THE EMOTIONAL IMPACT LETTER

An extremely helpful tool in developing empathy is for the partner to write her an emotional impact letter. This process originated out of *Facing Heartbreak—Steps to Recovery for Partners of Sex Addicts*. This tool is an important adjunct to the formal disclosure because it helps a partner to find her voice and to make sure she is heard. It gives her a safe place to share her thoughts, feelings and pain while the addict quietly listens. It is a great opportunity for empathy. This can be done several weeks after a formal disclosure has occurred, facilitated by 1-2 trained therapists.

Once she has participated in the disclosure and heard the truth, she is to write about how her spouse's actions have affected her. This typically results in her highlighting times when her spouse had deceived, manipulated, and gaslighted her. She may describe the anguish of being abandoned during the birth of their second child or being left at home during an appendicitis attack to fend for herself, or not being able to find her husband when their teenage daughter was in a near fatal car accident.

The impact may have included the pain of feeling increasing separation, never having sex anymore, the many nights she would wake up and he would be downstairs "surfing the INTERNET" when he was really engulfed in webchats and pornography.

This letter is a way to convey the pain and is a direct result of what she heard in the disclosure. It is a formalized way to give her pain "voice" and it is very cathartic for her. The addict's responsibility is to stay quiet and listen to her pain. He will then use the information to write a restitution letter. The partner reports feeling like she has found a safe way to purge the pain in a contained safe place. It almost always provides a sense of relief, and it provides a profound opportunity for the addict to show empathy when he completes his restitution letter.

THE RESTITUTION LETTER

The restitution letter is not an amends but an opportunity to share his responsibility for creating so much sadness and for hurting her. He is acknowledging what he did and the pain he caused her, yet he is not asking forgiveness. He receives a copy of her emotional impact letter and uses that to write his restitution letter. He is expected to have his letter ready for her within 2 weeks of her emotional impact letter.

It allows him to show her that he heard and acknowledges her pain. It creates an opportunity for her to feel validated and reaffirmed. It is a wonderful chance for the addict and partner to put closure on the secrets and to begin to rebuild their relationship.

NOTE: Not all partners want a formal disclosure and it is her prerogative as to whether she wants or needs one. This applies to the emotional impact and restitution letters as well.

I have used Early Couple's Recovery work to do the emotional impact letter and restitution letter without the disclosure. It is an equally powerful empathy exercise! When a partner has a safe space to share her anger and pain, she is able to get clear about her feelings and then decide what she is going to do about them. When the addict allows her uninterrupted time to share feelings, and then is able to address each and every point, she again feels heard and validated; she feels a bit safer to connect.

CHAPTER 11

RITUALS THAT PROMOTE CONNECTION, TRUST AND

RESTORATION OF THE RELATIONSHIP

EMPATHY EXERCISES TO ENHANCE COMMUNICATION

THE CONNECTION-SHARE©: A TIME TO CONNECT AND SHARE

To develop empathy, you have to know how to put yourself in your wife's shoes. Yet addicts do not necessarily know how to do this naturally. For many addicts, they need to practice developing the art of empathy. Not only are they not able to read her mind, it would be dangerous to do so because they might get it wrong and miss the opportunity of knowing what she thinks or feels. As a couple, you need more opportunities to check in with each other to find out what is going on in the heads and hearts of each other.

Your relationship requires a lot of repair, and another way to reassure your wife of your progress is to create a daily ritual whereby you spend 5 to 15 minutes sharing your highlights and struggles with each other for that particular day.

Check-ins have been used for decades by the addiction community to hold the addict accountable with his sponsor or fellowship.

There are various check–ins that you can follow, but I advocate for a check in that I call "The Connection-Share©".

THE CONNECTION-SHARE© CHECK–IN

The format for The Connection-Share is simple. It is important for you to customize them for your comfort level. Most partners want to know what their husbands are struggling with so that they will stay aware of his issues. However, if the partner feels this is too activating, she may ask him to share this daily with his sponsor, and she may choose some alternative "connection statements" that are equally disclosing and connecting.

Remember that whenever you are communicating, it is important to sit and watch each other to pick up non-verbal signs and cues that will enhance communication.

You both sit down face-to-face, and you check in with these five statements:

- Your primary feeling that you experienced today

- A struggle/concern that you encountered

- An appreciation for your recovery

- An appreciation for your relationship

- What you would like to work on for tomorrow's recovery

This format would look like this:

Your primary feeling that you experienced today:

- Sex Addict (SA): I had a good day today and mostly felt glad to be in recovery and to be working on our marriage.

A struggle/concern that you encountered:

- I struggled with feeling edgy this morning and was not able to pinpoint why I was emotionally out of sorts.

An appreciation for your recovery:

- I couldn't wait to get to my meeting today as I could sense that I was edgy, and I just knew that if I had a chance to listen to others and check in I would feel better.

An appreciation for your relationship:

- I know this is going to sound silly, but it felt deceiving that I didn't let you know that I was having an off-day. I didn't want to worry you, and yet something kept saying that Tami would want to know. I guess I was wanting to get some reassurance from you, and yet I avoided that because I did not want to trigger you even though my therapist has told me to start sharing my emotional self with you. I guess what I am saying here is that I appreciated that we are still together and that I thought about texting you and that I am sharing it now.

What you would like to work on for tomorrow's recovery?

- I am going to spend more time journaling what is going on with me internally so that I can connect to you more fully and be more vulnerable. Guess I need to read more Brené Brown, huh?

Here is an excerpt from a partner's Connection-Share:

Your primary feeling that you experienced today:

- Partner: I felt anxious today.

A struggle/concern that you encountered:

- I had to meet with my boss, and I have not been on my game for months since our disclosure, and I wondered if she sensed that I am not running on all cylinders. I hate that my mental state has been compromised.

An appreciation for your recovery:

- I can tell that I am slowly getting better. I hesitate to tell you this because I don't want you to think that you are off the hook, but I am forcing myself to be honest so that we can get better quicker, and I know that means that I have to trust you again. I am glad that I am taking that risk. Please don't let me down.

An appreciation for your relationship:

- I appreciate that we are talking more than we ever have for years. For so long I felt shut out of your life, and I couldn't figure out why, and now I can tell that you are working hard to make things right.

What you would like to work on for tomorrow's recovery?

- I would like to call my sponsor when I feel triggered. I try to handle it myself which invariably adds to the anger I feel towards you for causing the trigger in the first place. I think there is a part of me that doesn't want to take you off the hook. I want you to see how bad I feel because this pain is unbearable at times.

CHECK-INS REQUIRE VULNERABILITY AND NON-DEFENSIVENESS

It is important to do check-ins with an open heart. You must hear what your partner says and stay open to her feelings and thoughts without going into your shame spiral. When you hear her concerns, fears, and progress you will be better able to move forward and put yourself in her shoes and even anticipate what she feels.

Over time, people with good empathy skills know what is going on in the minds of their partners. Of course, it is always good to check in with her emotions and thoughts to see if you are on target.

Do these exercises daily so that you make time to connect and share. At first, it might feel like you are inviting conflict into your life because it may feel like another opportunity for your partner to vent about her pain. Yet by listening to her check-in, you will be able to find other times in the days to come to let her know that you get how she is feeling which will make her feel more connected.

REMEMBER, YOUR JOB IN THIS RELATIONSHIP RECOVERY IS TO HELP HER HEAL SO THAT YOU WILL FEEL LIKE YOU ARE REPAIRING THE RELATIONSHIP AND CONTRIBUTING TO THE RESTORATION WHICH SHOULD MAKE YOU FEEL BETTER ABOUT YOU.

If you have done these exercises with regularity, you might want to create some of your own Connection-Shares. Make sure that you both agree on them and that they feel safe for both of you. It is likely that there will be some things that you will want to know about each other that may lend itself to conflict. As your relationship becomes healthier, you should be able to handle the questions. As I indicated earlier, "In healthy relationships, conflict breeds intimacy."

I recognize that you don't want to invite conflict because you are so desirous of closeness.

Eventually you will be able to use Connections-Shares like the following:

- What I trust most about you is...

- What I trust least about you is ...

- What I appreciate most about you is ...

- What I most fear for our future is ...

- What I dream for the future is ...

- I felt _____ when I was triggered for no reason today.

- I need you to _____.

As your recovery strengthens, you will likely be able to understand your partner's feelings and anticipate her feelings and reactions. It can be helpful to check in with issues where you might sense that she would be triggered or have issues and let her know that you are paying attention to her needs.

She will likely be surprised about your thoughts and feelings about your relationship or your recovery. This process really opens up communication and starts the process of empathy building.

THE MIRROR EXERCISE

This is an exercise where the partner gets 3-5 minutes to speak without any interruptions. She can choose any topic that she would like to elaborate and often feels that she does not need the allotted time because when a woman has uninterrupted time to talk, she can concisely describe her thoughts and feelings without the need to defend herself. The other exciting thing about this process is that the addict is there to then repeat back exactly what he heard without editorializing or defending himself, so it teaches him the process of listening as opposed to reacting.

This exercise is a lot harder than it looks because couples have not been taught to listen to the other person with the sole outcome to repeat what s/he said. This exercise mandates that you repeat what you heard verbatim ... no paraphrasing!

KNEES–TO–KNEES EXERCISE

When you touch each other in a non-threatening way, you are more likely to be open to each other and hear the communication with less internal dialogue. This exercise requires that you ask the partner if she would be willing to allow each one of you to make contact by touching knees. If she says yes, then you proceed with your communication and make physical contact.

It is easy to sit on the couch and talk about important things and not really give each other eye contact. Make it a commitment as a couple to never again communicate without facing each other and touching knees-to-knees. Touching knees is a safe, non-sexual way to make physical contact.

The 2nd prerequisite of this exercise is that you look at each other face-to-face, eye-to-eye, so that you can watch their reactions and nonverbal cues. Empathy requires that you put yourself in your partner's shoes, which means you need to attentively work on assessing what you believe may be going on as the two of you discuss issues.

Many couples attempt to communicate while they are multi-tasking and your relationship requires that both of you be present. If you are discussing something that is emotionally charged, it will be important to watch for triggers so that you can practice Trigger Busters. If you are sincerely working on empathy, you will want to watch her facial reactions to validate her feelings.

If you sincerely want to repair this relationship, you will need to put 200% into it. Every opportunity that you have to connect will require extreme attention. Many sex addicts have Attention Deficit Disorder (ADD) or symptoms that mimic ADD, and as a result, they miss a lot of important cues.

You will need to stay present, stay focused and watch for cues that will help you to empathize with her.

IF YOU SINCERELY WANT TO REPAIR THIS RELATIONSHIP, YOU WILL NEED TO PUT 200% INTO IT—EVERY OPPORTUNITY YOU HAVE—AND THAT REQUIRES EXTREME ATTENTION.

ON A SCALE OF 1 TO 10, HOW WOULD YOU RATE YOUR RELATIONSHIP?

This exercise is an easy way to assess your relationship from your partners perspective. You can use it as part of your Connection-Share or you can ask the question when you are in the car with your spouse or walking the dog together.

If you use it as part of a dialogue, I would encourage you to use your communication skills and give each other full attention.

The exercise came from Jack Canfield's *The Success Principles*. He would regularly use it with his wife to gauge what they needed to work on in their relationship.

FACING EACH OTHER, KNEE-TO-KNEE

On a scale of 1-10, explain how you feel your relationship is going. What would it take to advance to the next number? This means that you check in with each other and say to the partner:

- SA: "How would you rate the quality of our relationship today?"

- PA: "I would rate the quality of our relationship a 6 today."

- SA: "What would it take to make it a 7?"

- PA: I would like for you to find me when you get home and give me a hug that at least lasts for 30 seconds.

- SA: I will remind myself to do that daily.

Then the PA asks the SA the same initial question so that each person gets time to identify a behavioral request that improves the relationship.

These techniques are imperative in restoring the trust, closeness, and security in your fractured relationship. As you practice them regularly, you will see a gradual change in your coupleship. John Gray Ph.D calls it "making investments in each other's love tank."

As you hear each other's answers, ask yourself the following questions:

- What are my core beliefs about our relationship?

- What will it take to make things better or turn things around?

- What do I need to hear from her?

- What do I need to share about myself?

CONCLUSION

> "ONE DOESN'T HAVE TO OPERATE WITH GREAT MALICE TO DO GREAT HARM.
> THE ABSENCE OF EMPATHY AND UNDERSTANDING ARE SUFFICIENT."
> — CHARLES M. BLOW

Completing this workbook has insured that you are on the road to understanding your partner and showing her that you "get her." When I talk to partners, they "hands down" say the #1 thing they want from him, besides recovery, is to know that he gets her and the trauma that he caused. You have learned the relational skills to convey that to her!

You did it! You finished the workbook!

We want to commend you for doing this hard work. You bought this book because you wanted to show your spouse that you heard her when she told you that you did not fully understand her pain! You went the extra mile to do the tough work to become a better partner. You will never be able to erase what you have done, but you have chosen to become a better communicator and empathizer. You truly want to be the supportive spouse she deserves. As you work through the process of being there for your wife, you will feel better about your own self-worth. The process of empathy pays big time dividends, but you have to work it!

When You Work It ... it works!

Don't Stop Here.

Now it is time for you to do the hard work and practice what you have read and learned daily. We designed this workbook to help you to chart the feelings, thoughts, and actions of both you and your spouse. It has been broken down in steps that we hope you will practice with diligence. What we believe is that you probably did not possess many of these skills prior to your addiction and that they were not a priority while you were in active addiction. You need to make up for lost time, and this book can serve as a primer for "Putting yourself in her shoes."

Stay Focused on Your Progress

One of my coaching principles is to be grateful for what is working! As you do this work, make sure to notice the progress in your relationship. When you use these relational skills, they will make a difference in your functioning. I can't emphasize enough that you need to have gratitude for what is working!

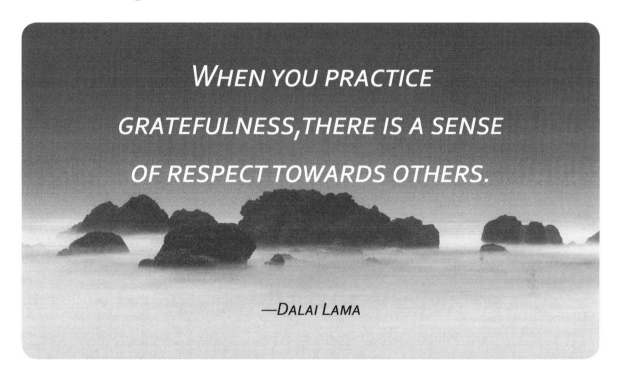

WHEN YOU PRACTICE GRATEFULNESS, THERE IS A SENSE OF RESPECT TOWARDS OTHERS.

—DALAI LAMA

Don't Do It Alone

It is important for you to find a certified sexual addiction therapist (CSAT) for yourself to support you on this journey. You can do this by going to sexhelp.com. This website has IITAP trained therapists who are specialists at working with sexual addiction.

You can also go to SASH: The Society for the Advancement of Sexual Health and find therapists who specialize in problematic sexual behavior.

If you believe that your wife is suffering from the trauma that you have caused her, you will need a therapist who has been trained by APSATS because her therapist needs to be partner sensitive and to be able to make your spouse a top priority in the healing process of sexual addiction. To find an APSATS trained partner therapist or coach go to APSATS.org and look for someone in your area.

IN CONCLUSION,

Sexual addiction is a relational issue, and developing good relational skills is imperative to restoring your relationship and your life. You have taken a major step in working on the healing that needs to occur after the discovery of sexual addiction. Continue to practice these skills and she will slowly feel safe to trust the healing process that needs to occur to rebuild the relationship. These skills will make you a better spouse, father and human being.

Have patience with her and with yourself. We have seen thousands of men do the work with their spouse and recommit to their relationship in new and exciting ways.

Stay strong in your recovery and stay the relational course. You can restore the relationship and create the life you both deserve!

We believe in you and the work you are doing!

—"Carol the Coach" and Allan J. Katz

The purpose that you wish to find in life,
like a cure you seek,
is not going to fall from the sky…
I believe purpose is something
for which one is responsible;
it's not just divinely assigned.

———

—Michael J. Fox

FOR YOUR THERAPIST

If you are already in therapy and you want to continue with a therapist who is not trained in sexual addiction or partner sensitive therapy, you might want to share this workbook with him or her to assist you in developing these skills.

Here is a primer for your therapist that you can tear out and ask them to use as a guideline for your therapy if you are considering doing empathy or couple's work. Hopefully it will help the therapist to support you through the process of helping the coupleship heal.

So, make sure to share the following guidelines with your therapist to make sure that you are all working together for the sake of the partner and your relationship.

Early Recovery Couples Work should never be done if the following prerequisites are not in place.

EARLY RECOVERY COUPLES WORK REQUIREMENTS:

The addict must be in a recovery program including 12-step groups, sponsor and therapy, and he must show active recovery progress. I recommend at least 90 days of working a solid program so that he gets the tools he needs in his recovery and with his fellowship to handle the stress that he feels from his spouse likely feeling great trauma about the discovery and his new-found recovery.

1. There needs to be a full disclosure by at least one, but preferably two therapists that have been trained in partner sensitive disclosures.

2. The addict is to take a polygraph within 48 hours of the disclosure to ensure the legitimacy of the disclosure.

3. The partner is to write an emotional impact letter

4. Addict is to respond with a restitution letter.

5. The addict should receive regular polygraph exams every 4 to 6 months for the first year.

QUESTIONS FOR THE ADDICT'S THERAPIST:

1. Is the addict in good recovery?

2. Does his recovery program include a 12-step group or a recovery program, a sponsor or a mentor?

3. Is he actively working the steps or doing coaching through another program?

4. Is he motivated to assist his partner in her healing?

5. Does he have a good support system to promote empathy with his partner?

QUESTIONS FOR THE PARTNER'S THERAPIST:

1. Is the partner working on self-soothing to decrease the intensity and frequency of her triggers?

2. Is she willing to accept her partner's imperfections (not active addiction)?

3. Can she set boundaries with consequences?

4. Does she have and use a support system?

As the Therapist, You Can Assist the Addict in Having a Partner Sensitive Perspective:

1. Does the addict that you work with know and acknowledge he caused his partner's pain & is directly responsible for it?

2. Does he have the tools to help him not descend into a shame spiral when his partner rejects him?

3. Is the addict willing to learn to decrease his shame?

4. Is the addict willing to deal with the storming that will naturally occur in the relationship?

5. Is the addict willing to improve the partner's sense of safety which restores his self-esteem?

6. Is your client willing to participate in at least one year of Early Recovery Couple's Work to learn the basic skills of empathy, communication, and trigger reduction?

7. Is the addict willing to support his spouse's grief and mourning of the relationship that she thought she had?

8. Can the addict be patient with her as she mourns and grieves the relationship?

9. Will the addict have faith that the relationship can weather the fracturing which has occurred?

As a Partner Sensitive Therapist, are you willing to work with the partner to help her with the following needs?

1. Will you help the partner determine if she is going to stay in the relationship?

2. Will the partner look for ways to restore the coupleship?

3. Is she willing to learn to self-regulate?

4. Can she notice and acknowledge the improvements in the addict?

5. Will you be able to help your client safely let her guard down enough to appreciate the changes?

END NOTES

Chapter 1

- Carnes, Patrick. *Recovery Start Kit*, CD. Gentle Path Press: Phoenix, Arizona. 2006.

Chapter 2

- Brené Brown. *Daring Greatly: How the Courage to Be Vulnerable Transforms the Way We Live, Love, Parent and Lead*. Avery Publishing: New York City, New York. 2012.

- Gottman, John. *The Seven Principles for Making Marriage Work*. Harmony Books: New York City, New York. 2000
  [Also referenced in Chapters 4 & 6]

Chapter 4

- *Managing Triggers of Betrayal*, chart. www.ChristinaBell.net.

- *Relational CPR* with Permission from Dorit Reichental and Janice Caudill.

Chapter 6

- Freyd, Jennifer. *Betrayal Trauma: The Logic of Forgetting Childhood Abuse*. Harvard University Press: Cambridge MA. 1996.

Chapter 9

- Chapman, Gary. *The Five Love Languages: How to Express Heartfelt Commitment to Your Mate*. Northfield Publishing: Chicago, Illinois. 1995.

- Lewis, Dawn Laura. *The Eight Stages of Intimacy*, 2004.

Chapter 10

- Carnes, Stefanie, Lee, Mari A., Rodriguez, & Anthony D. *Facing Heartbreak: Steps to Recovery for partners of Sex Addicts*. Gentle Path Press: Phoenix, Arizona. 2010.

ABOUT THE AUTHORS

Carol Juergensen Sheets LCSW, PCC, CSAT, CCPS brings a variety of experiences to the community, including having worked in schools, hospitals and in mental health for over 35 years. She has devoted the last two decades to helping men and women manage their sex addiction and by helping betrayed partners work through the trauma of sexual and relational betrayal. Carol is a trainer for the Association of Partners of Sex Addicts Trauma Specialists and is a consultant for clinicians and coaches at APSATS. She is also a certified sex addiction therapist (CSAT) through IITAP.

Carol completed her master's degree at Indiana University School of Social Work. She is currently facilitating workshops on relationships both statewide and nationally.

You can read over 500 articles on her website at www.carolthecoach.com or go to her sex addiction website for sex addicts or partners at www.sexhelpwithcarolthecoach.com

Carol appears regularly on television and radio. She was the first to host a radio show on sexual addiction on iTunes and has over 600,000 open downloads per week. Her current INTERNET show can be accessed by going to www.blogtalkradio.com/sexhelpwithcarol-thecoach.

She also hosts a partner betrayal show on *Betrayal Recovery Radio* for APSATS at www.blogtalkradio/betrayalrecoveryradio.com

Carol is married to her husband Eric. She enjoys traveling, paddle boarding and taking long walks with her husband and her dog "Boo Bear."

Allan J. Katz LPC, CSAT known as the "Healthy Intimacy Coach," helps individuals and couples foster healthy intimacy, improve communication and stop addiction.

Allan is the author of two books, *Addictive Entrepreneurship*, and *Experiential Group Therapy Interventions with DBT: A 30 day program for treating addictions and trauma*. He is a Licensed Professional Counselor and a Certified Sex Addiction Therapist. For the past six years, he has worked as a group and individual counselor in a drug and alcohol rehab center in Southaven, Mississippi. He now exclusively counsels private individuals and couples for relationship and intimacy issues, addictions and trauma resolution in Memphis, Tennessee.

Mr. Katz trains other therapists on using experiential therapy methods in group work for treating addictions and trauma and is available to speak at conferences, clubs and meetings.

SEXUAL ADDICTION
Wisdom from The Masters

Compiled by
Carol the Coach
Carol Juergensen Sheets LCSW CSAT

This book shares the wisdom from the most prolific sexual addiction experts in the world talking about sexual addiction, shame, trauma, trauma reenactment, partner betrayal, partner pain, love addiction, and other issues that contribute to compulsive sexual acting out.

Two of the chapters include Patrick Carnes who founded the Sexual Addiction Recovery Movement and Claudia Black who helps Partners of Sex Addicts regain their equilibrium from this traumatic disorder. This book simplifies the principles that make recovery possible for anyone who has been affected by sexual addiction.

If you believe that you have a sexual addiction or you love someone who suffers from this addiction, you will benefit from reading the recovery tasks that will take your life to the next level! Available today at carolthecoach.com/products.

Additional Material by Carol Juergensen Sheets LCSW, PCC, CSAT, CCPS:

- Creative Coaching: 65 Empowerment Secrets to Create the Life you Deserve!

- Creative Coaching: 65 Empowerment Exercises to Coach Your Client into Excellence

- Shortcuts to Creating Positive Self-Esteem

- Improving Relationships: A Couple's Workbook

Group Work for Men in Sexual Recovery

A Strategic Model for Sex Addicts

Carol Juergensen Sheets, LCSW, CSAT
Carol the Coach

Historically, sex addicts have had to rely on individual therapy and 12-Step support to enhance their recovery. Group work is a crucial element to recovery but is typically only provided in residential and hospital settings. Addicts have often times been traumatized early in their own childhoods, and group intervention provides the supportive environment to do out patient trauma work.

This manual will highlight group exercises that have been essential to therapeutic change and recovery. It utilizes a 15-week approach to managing anger, conflict and trauma. It teaches empathy and assertiveness so that the client can improve his or her relationships outside of the therapeutic alliance.

This book is for clinicians who want a hands-on approach to running a sexual addiction group. It will take you from week 1 through week 15 giving you exercises to promote therapeutic change and recovery. Available today at carolthecoach.com/products.

Available Today at carolthecoach.com/products!

- Setting Goals Creates Success

- Finding Your God-Given Dream

- Group Work for Women

Made in the USA
San Bernardino, CA
31 July 2019